'*Candles and Water* risks everything, daring to explore powerful vulnerabilities, yearning, and unabashed hope. Elusiveness and the whisperings of shadows inhabit these pages, always illuminated and burnished by the voice of a poet.'

THOMAS GLAVE

'Timothy Thornton's *Candles and Water* is a rare and transformational book, haunting, beautiful and watchful. Writing that follows its brush like Sei Shōnagon.'

DAVID HAYDEN

CANDLES AND WATER

Timothy Thornton

Candles and Water

Front cover image: Richard Porter
35mm film photograph from personal archive, 2023

Reverse cover image: Keith Vaughan
'Boy Holding Up Fishing Net,' 1939

ISBN 978-1-7393649-9-1

Published in the U.K. by Pilot Press

Printed on 100% recycled paper

for

E.B.—S.C.—C.D.—J.D.

In a garden full of evergreens the crows are all asleep. Then, towards the middle of the night, the crows in one of the trees suddenly wake up in a great flurry and start flapping about. Their unrest spreads to the other trees, and soon all the birds have been startled from their sleep and are cawing in alarm. How different from the same crows in daytime!

Sei Shōnagon

Screwed at its axis against the side, a swinging lamp slightly oscillates in Jonah's room; and the ship, heeling over towards the wharf with the weight of the last bales received, the lamp, flame and all, though in slight motion, still maintains a permanent obliquity with reference to the room; though, in truth, infallibly straight itself, it but made obvious the false, lying levels among which it hung.

Father Mapple

FLOTSAM

1 The brittleness started

The brittleness started suddenly with a sentient and quasar-sized samphire, nestled very distantly on the unthinkable shore of something enormous, unsayable what, rockpools pocking fresh and clear around it bigger than galaxies and everything calm for the longest recorded while but then this. One day just there.

The brittleness started scaling by a factor of a migraine, to the power of a migraine, a migraine to the power of a migraine times, fearful brokenness spooling out on the thread of an infinite spiral unwinding, for no possible reason, and so unreasonably beautiful.

We were all very sad, to learn of this. The universe was tense for a time, until the news was no longer new. And there remains as there would an aura of exhaustion, as if legitimate dread already but then this. Still people touched by an invisible capillary keep looking in its direction without realizing they are doing so. We think people think they are thinking, or remembering, when they do that.

You are brittle. Involuntarily you are looking across great distances to a convulsion of unimaginable fragility, where the sob truly started. Not, as it may have felt, deep in the cave of your chest.

2 A very short introduction to ghosts

Have you ever seen a ghost? On the way home I saw a ghost, just today. Do you know what a ghost is? You probably think a ghost is somebody who has died. Somebody who has died, yet for some reason is still here, just a little. Maybe they are still here, just a little, because they are angry, or sad, or even just very lost or very stuck.

Some ghosts are supposed to be harmless, or even very kind, and some are supposed to be downright evil. Some are naughty, and cause trouble, they blow curtains about and throw things. They're called poltergeists. But all of that is just a lie. Ghosts are people who remind people of nobody.

Have you ever seen someone in the street and you thought you knew them? Sometimes months go past without that happening, but sometimes it happens three times in one day. Have you ever been so sure it was someone you knew that you actually said hello?

Sometimes the opposite happens. You're absolutely sure you recognised them, but then you can't figure out who they reminded you of. Sometimes this is fine, because you figure it out a few minutes later, or a few hours later. But sometimes, it's like when you are watching a film, and you recognise an actor, but you can't remember what else they've been in. And you forget to pay attention to the rest of the film, because you are trying so hard to remember what other film or television programme you've seen this actor in.

And for days you are bothered by trying to figure out who this person reminded you of. You may remember in the end. Sometimes we can all be very forgetful. But if you remember, that isn't a ghost.

If you have seen a ghost, you figure out, in the end, that they reminded you of nobody. Nobody you have never met. And later on with a shudder, you realise that they reminded you of somebody who does not exist and never has.

What can that mean? It doesn't make sense. But the person they reminded you of, so vividly and so unmistakably, doesn't exist, definitely doesn't exist, and definitely never has existed. You don't know how you know this, but you just know it. More certain than anything you've ever known. And you will only know this feeling if you have seen a ghost, because you suddenly turn very very cold, and your skin goes prickly and tight, and the hairs stand up on the back of your neck, and for a few seconds you feel like you might never see the sun again.

In your mind there are millions and millions of memories, but they are all of something. What happens when you see a ghost is you are reminded of something which is nothing. It makes a memory in your mind of something which is nothing. And your mind is not used to having a pocket of nothing in it.

That's why you suddenly turn so very cold, and why your skin goes so prickly and so tight, and why the hairs on the back of your neck stand up, and why for a few seconds you feel so much like you might never see the sun again. Because there is now a hole in your mind.

The thing about ghosts is they don't last very long. Everyone becomes a ghost a few times in their life, just for a second, a split second when they remind somebody they have never met of nobody. And do you know what else is true? Nobody knows they are a ghost, when they are a ghost. At some point in your life, you will be on the other, darker side of the street, and you will remind somebody of nobody, very briefly, and you won't feel a thing, and you will probably never know about it.

The last thing to say about seeing a ghost is that the hole in your mind stays there forever. And it's a new hole each time. The more ghosts you see, the more holes in your mind there are. So if you see hundreds and hundreds of ghosts, your mind has more and more holes in it, and it slowly becomes nothing, and you slowly become nobody.

And who is more likely, from the other, darker side of the street, to remind somebody they have never met of nobody, than someone who is gradually becoming no one?

3 The moth

It was in the second half of the nineteenth century, during an otherwise familiar and unremarkable dream about maps of dreams, that a new and worrying map, with some very unusual properties, was discovered: it was a map of a dream about maps of dreams, itself of course featuring locations which represented dreams, within the dream represented on the map, about maps of dreams; these little glitches brought to bear on the top-level dream texture those threats, either of a diminishing recursiveness, or of a sudden erosion or porosity in an otherwise familiar and unremarkable concentricity of realities, which can lead in the worst cases to waking up confused, and even frightened; they were improperly marked on the map because no adequate symbol had yet been discovered, and it was for exactly this purpose that the courtesan, when she awoke from the dream, devised the moth—to this day the marker of a sinkhole between realities, which can lead if mishandled to the creation of inward-plunging dream-worlds never to be escaped from, or, in the worst case, to waking up confused, and even frightened, having sincerely believed that you had already done so.

4 The image

The image, vivid but unsourceable as far as I can figure, of a twilit field, very dark, not very moonlit, viewed from very low on the ground, mud everywhere and yellowing grass and generally rotting matter, about five inches deep in slushy dark liquid, a field vivid with watery and enzymatic decay, and full also of hundreds of cows, silhouetted against the heavy blue of the sky, and who haven't moved for weeks, just stood there, and who are beginning—through foot rot, or fetlock rot, or leg rot, whatever it is called when some ripe-scented liquefactive necrosis extends further and further up—to melt away into the mud, not so much sinking as being very slowly eroded or digested from the hooves upward: yet every time I return to this image, the cows haven't sunk any further; it seems to me that their future has always to be implied, and it is impossible or forbidden to see them any later on, only to open a new window, visit a new image of a similar scene, some field of cows who in their reality have only just begun to melt. They do not at least seem to be in any distress, and they are bothered by fewer flies than you'd think.

5 In a building somewhere

In a building somewhere next to the Thames, I can't remember where, there is a metal rod which runs in a thin brass cylinder from the sixth floor, through all the other floors, down to the river, or at least to a chamber where river-water collects. It moves, according to the movement of the tides, upward and downward, very slightly, almost imperceptibly. The building is or was used for office space and most people on the sixth floor weren't even aware of the metal rod, let alone what its movement meant. Certainly nobody was aware, when sometimes they pressed it out of curiosity, that the mechanism reversed and, very slightly, the moon slowed down. Just for a moment.

6 Hold

A more recent local legend, specific to the elderly, involved those who repeatedly, on finishing a call on a mobile telephone, would find they had walked to the sea, as if their lack of familiarity with newer communications technology somehow brought out the river in them. If any of these people were placed on hold as they walked, they were done for, since their call got lost in the system when they got to the seafront, as soon as they touched the water.

As far as the other party was concerned, the call had been terminated. The elderly person on the phone remained on hold, hearing the same looped music crackly and tinny as they walked out to sea. In the marina sometimes, down the slope, though mostly just into the sea. Everyone we asked said the same: you'd never get them back after that.

Multiple networks have confirmed that there are calls still connected which fit such a path, and which have remained connected for many years, from handsets located miles offshore and however many fathoms deep.

From all of this, we can conclude not only that these 'hold ghosts' still somehow get phone signal, even stood on the sea bed, but also that their handsets must become impervious to water damage, and gain an implausible battery-life.

They told us that the music most frequently found to be looping in these calls is Vivaldi. The calls, we did ask, cannot be disconnected.

7 Hastings

On Wednesdays you used to be able to drive down onto the beach, right the way down, and sit in your car with the sea behind you, and look up above the cliffs, at a firework display. They did it in all weathers. Rain could be gently snaking down your windscreen, rain could be hammering down so hard you'd have the wipers on and barely be able to see the fireworks, but you'd still be able to drive down onto the beach and watch the firework display, blurred and smeared.

I used to do this while testing the capacity of the roof of my mouth to withstand the heat of a McDonald's apple pie against my eagerness to eat it, which though it may be unwise and painful is nevertheless something you can do without too much looking down, so it did not involve my missing the firework display. I was young, too young to drive, so someone else drove the car, and there were fireworks, and too-hot food at the end of the journey.

There must somewhere in the above story be a half-truth, some inaccuracy sneaked through, because in my head, the corruption of a memory, for better or worse, is accompanied by something like that sound made when someone working in a pub empties all the glass bottles into a large bin out the back. It's the loudest thing, and it never fails to startle. Despite the fact that this noise is constant: you can imagine.

Those corruptions don't require the accessing of a memory; the stories just fall apart or drift slightly, somewhere in the back of my brain, a hundred times a second, and I know it is happening because of the constant noise of glass bottles being poured into a bin, which is at least as intense as the cliffs crumbling and splitting into blizzards of rock and dust as they fell onto the car and pushed it with great creaking and scraping noises backwards into the sea, and the pressure to push above the noise of it and keep talking now is at least as intense as the pressure that cracked the windscreen as we went further back into the water, which as it rose around us covered our eyes and ears and blurred and smeared the firework display into nothing worth remembering.

There was also a small roller-coaster near the seafront, it looked like a dragon, which survived the cliff-fall.

8 The ghost cat

The ghost cat who visits my room hasn't been about lately. I've never seen it, but sometimes, for a while, the door would open, or some garment or other fabric would seem to have flattened a little, or to have slightly changed position.

I don't think it's any cat I have known while it was alive, though sometimes I feel differently about that. It hasn't made any noise at any point. Not deliberately. It did once knock over an empty lager can.

None of my previous research into ghosts, fog, dust, headlands, inaccessible light-sources, defunct mechanisms, finches, maps, foxes, or bodies of water, has been useful in communicating with the cat. Even the 'chirrup' which cats produce on entering a room, which has long been known to be a noise cats make only for the benefit of their human companions, is entirely absent here.

It has been ascertained that dogs bark in order to check whether they are still alive. Even in the case of those barks which we supposed were intended for us, the primary function still operates. Dogs which are ghosts can still bark, but we rarely hear it; perhaps they hear so quickly that they are ghosts that the bark is curtailed immediately, in surprise or fear.

Now, ghosts which are cats, which is to say, defunct cat-mechanisms which are bodies of ghosts subject tidally to the open lake of a raised floor, are an absent chirrup. Sometimes a fabric flattens and do you miss anyone, such as cats. Inaccessibly fog dust. To double-check the ramified map of how alive I am, barked back a fog. Through you a dog is pecked. Chirrup.

Open water between a light source and how dust is become a headland, do you see. Yet how an interim is a fox headland or phrased differently not yet inaccessible is the crucial map: the eyes of ghost cats splinter into a mirrored network, the light source distantly reflected, almost certainly the flicker of ghost water meeting itself along a shear.

Open ghosts flicker to check they are interstitial, the opposite cat-mechanism to a body of defunct water unpouring yet and where tidally must the light sources eye by eye be reintroduced. A gull by any other angle of incidence retires the itinerary into once again, is it alive, the flicker of open water meeting a willed unhaunting silently and without feedback, a brief headland become immediately dust, in defunct surprise or inaccessible fear.

9 Breath and the roar

Of what must be a limitless number of coincidences in timing whose nature comes after the fact to seem quite cavernous, our focus here is that which occurs when you are half sleeping, in bed with a wholly sleeping lover, and have allowed your hearing to settle and slow to the rhythm of their breathing, acutely aware of any increase in intensity, any approach toward that tiniest excess of pressure which would tip the breathing over some quite physical threshold or cliff and render it a snoring, when suddenly, after a silent pause or trough, a new inhalation seems to continue, and continue and continue and continue, until it has become something completely new, and you realize that in some intricated and very personal concomitance of timing, just for you, the calm intake of breath to which you are the only auditor has become a bracing traffic roar, the car outside already gone away as quickly as you could figure its identity, and your ears, deaf to parallax because of pillows and the sharp attention to the rhythms of your oblivious lover, have confused the breath and the roar, before the passing car was close enough for breath and roar to be distinct in any case; and next there are the gaps which appear, the tearings-apart which happen in the last two seconds of your memory, between the car and your lover, and the breath, and the noise, and the point at which the breath had become so loud and violent that the elastic of your believing in it as a breath was snapped, and some other understanding had then to fall into place, and the inside of your lover's chest opening up to take in more and more and more air as the breath became as vast as it could possibly become before the elastic of your believing in it as a breath was snapped; and all these instances, the world prying back by just a touch into your memory and in a funk of dilatory yawns opening up to you the wideness of the night, all these pullings-apart are so much the stranger for their being the result of two things happening at the same time.

10 Mr Khachatari's

There are no windows on Mr Khachatari's. There is a solid wooden door, painted a deep and dull red. At the top there is a brighter red sign with large white Times New Roman lettering saying 'MR KHACHATARI'S'. There is no other writing, nothing to identify what is or was sold there. 'Khachatari' doesn't seem to be a surname that exists.

Nobody ever goes in or out. There is a café over the road, which is the vantage I have on Mr Khachatari's. Always the same. More properly, it is a caff: Formica tables, plastic tomatoes full of ketchup, mismatched old mugs from obscure companies or recondite conferences, bearing phone numbers that look like they're from the nineties. Mugs which are not white on the inside, so that your tea looks subtly strange. The meniscus is not right. You can get something called a 'Breakfast Bap' which is an entire small fry-up crammed into a bread roll.

Sometimes, people in the caff talk about Mr Khachatari's, because it's visible across the road; but nobody knows anything about Mr Khachatari himself. The caff is next to a shabby old GP practice, entirely upstairs; the single door, when the receptionist buzzes you in, opens into a narrow, miserable stairwell.

So far as I know, not one person in the caff, staff or customer, has ever known who Mr Khachatari is, nor whether he even exists. Perhaps it is a made-up name. The shop sells, by some accounts, nothing, being a sort of ghost enterprise, something to do with taxes. By other accounts, it sells many things, even 'everything... like a lot of businesses round here'—this from a bleary-eyed man in hi-viz one morning, drenching his massive fry-up in brown sauce. Some people will hazard that Mr Khachatari's is simply defunct; some will tell you that things do happen there, but that they do not know what they are. Nobody has ever seen these goings-on themselves, it's always a second or third-hand story.

11 The crow

Something is flowing through you, from your head downward through your neck and chest and out arm by arm, finger by finger, then further down your trunk, and leg by leg, toe by toe, and so on; not so much a kind of golden light, or anything which might osmose from an angel wrapping his luminous, muscular wings around you, but a more ineffable humour, perhaps the marrow of that half-attentive black crow which, you remember, prevented you, by standing on your neck with its claws tugging at the skin above your veins, from sitting up or moving when you found yourself supine on the back seats of that dusty airless empty bus for days on end through some desert, wondering for long parched hours how the previously inert fungus you had been watching in your bedroom for weeks was suddenly able to extend in foot-long thin rods or wands out of the coffee mugs, meeting and joining each other in intricate hexagonal patterns, each such union marked by one tiny, sticky, glistening, bright red orb of spores, and wondering how thousands of the local children had by the evening of your departure come to be playing in the park with replicas of these rods or wands of fungus, and why the only way to win in the game these children were playing with these wands was to return after the distraction of a dropped ice cream to find that you had been eaten by a ghost in Pacman, and worrying that the marrow of this crow is not, honestly, fluid enough to flow through you at all without instead inducing in every one of the thousand neighbourhood children a brief hallucination, like those splintered out from a dream, of a closed and unlit universe entirely of vaults, a perpetual catacomb, cyclical and unvaried, deep in the marrow of a wingless, beakless crow, the final and blueprint crow, formed only of a single unsegmented bone, the shape of a torus, covered in black feathers which glistening and sticky way out there on the outer surface meet and join and flow through each other.

12 A visit

It was a little after 2 a.m. when something of the strong winds and the pitch-dark outside got in, through my window, and made itself known. I do not know what it was. I had got into bed having left a lit candle on my windowsill, with no other lights on, and the window slightly ajar as I had been smoking.

My bedroom at the time was on the first floor of the large vicarage on Washington Street. Hanover hill is steep, though, and I faced down it, meaning that to the ground outside my window was a drop of two or three storeys. To look out of it, you felt very high up. I had not lived there long, and had not yet fitted curtains. The candle flame had not previously been much bothered by the slightly open window, but now of course it was buffeted wildly, such that whatever entity this was arrived to a seemly riot of dancing shadows. No part of the room escaped them. Across near the wall, somewhere a few inches above the mantelpiece, and a few inches out into the room, where certainly there was nothing to make such a noise, was a quiet but bright metallic ding.

I knew something was present. I sat myself up in bed, with the duvet pulled right up to my neck, to properly acknowledge it, and be with it, whatever it was. I felt a little absurd, but I was also keen to behave very seriously. I sat tense and absolutely still for one or perhaps two minutes. I was concerned to be respectful and welcoming: whatever had got in did not feel threatening, but it was immensely powerful, and for sure was not to be messed with. The nature of its presence in the room changed, very gradually. I became aware that there was to be no interaction, no communication. But we were each, definitely, aware of the other. That's all I remember. It was a good experience, a reminder of magnificent things.

The following day, I had work in the evening. Come early afternoon, I was already absolutely shattered, and decided to attempt to recharge with a quick nap. I set an alarm, got naked, cursed myself for not having installed curtains yet—it was still light, even though it was winter—and jumped into bed in the hope I might fall asleep for at least a few minutes. I am no expert at naps, and in trying to help myself drift off I reached for the trick of thinking deliberately of relaxing situations, or of relaxing things.

Within a few seconds I found myself thinking of whatever it was that had stopped and stayed in my room for a while, in the night-time. I noticed that when I revisited that memory, despite finding it immense and incomprehensible, I also found it reassuring. Suddenly not three inches from my face a sharp smack on the pillow. Nothing was visible when I opened my eyes, which I did in an instant. Nothing was there. I had heard it, and I had felt it in the fabric. It had been right there. Perhaps it still was. And perhaps trying to 'use' the memory of its night-time presence, to help me to sleep the following afternoon—or for any reason at all—counted enough as 'messing' with it to warrant being told off. What I did know for sure is that the sharp smack on the pillow was not intended as a reassurance. I didn't sleep.

13 Kettle

Here is something I wrote, for no reason, an hour or two ago. I have changed some of the words, to make it different; and this introductory chute will flow straight into it without any deliberate marker of change such as a paragraph break, although perhaps the change in tone will be obvious. It doesn't really matter, because all that follows is really an advertisement for the substantial excellence even in difficult or confusing circumstances of those very heavy black cast-iron Japanese tea kettles; in many ways it is also a coded invitation for you to buy me one, because it would make me happy indeed, and although it would set you back financially you would I am sure be richer in spirit. Before I folded inward, I should say, I had recently seen and much loved a cast-iron Japanese tea kettle. I had felt its weight, and had wept that I too might be so comprehensively in the world. You can imagine then the reassurance when after a desperate and upsetting subsidence of mind I found that the void, when I arrived, had just such a kettle in it. Right enough, it extended through no space, and neither had I body nor mind yet there I was, shifting about for sure in the nothing, and somehow of it. I should say it was not dark. And there was no sense of being in a spaceless place which was at least internal to some other; none of that. A set of not-fully-menacing glyphs, which redrew themselves when observed, or unobserved, it was impossible to tell, although never in any case to anything comprehensible, persisted adjacently somehow. And of course as I have said there was this very heavy cast-iron tea kettle, which must have rested on something, though nothing seemed there. It was full, and there were two black cups, of stuff similar in weight (judging proportionally, by their size) to the kettle. The tea was white tea, delicate and subtle, and it seemed never to run out. I have no idea how it was that I smelled or poured it, let alone drank and tasted any, but still: I could winter here, I thought. It was then though that I remembered: it is summer, and I should not be here.

14 Sidings

My afternoon head has a ghost ache in it, something about jobs, driving me running like damp inks or obsolete software, but along a viaduct in the sun a death-watch beetle builds sheds, slatted and overindulged by the self-esteem of shadows which never got to do a weathervane or a trellis of finches; were you never then a brass rivet as I am, I said, on a shoulder on a siding on a sweating on a suntan, or other methods for your own incandescing alloy in a stairwell let rip like a word invented to mark down the noise of scaffolding rotating through its rusted self, leaving moon-bright shiny riflings round the joints? In that silo funnelling under there I can smell your armpit relevant among corrugated green rooves, have you never in ripping up bracken by the stem shredded with its cheesewires your hands into blood and skeins of flesh, printed them on the flaking metal of the yellow machinery as the sweat drips and fucked like still-blazed sunlight in a lengthened afternoon was apprenticed for? On the train with coffee about jobs you are not even on the railway, one day you did get naked on the sidings, but you were a teenager, even though he was not, and you felt like old pornography printed and discardable, and subject to erosion, and water damage, and discovery, and use, and repetition, and of course hi-viz jackets were to become as memorable in the sun as brass rivets or a glinting afternoon rail.

15 Phase

Outside my window as I write this there is a zebra crossing. I have had good views before, but this is the best man-made thing I have ever had outside my window, other than an offshore windfarm. The names of the different kinds of crossing refuse to stick in my head, but I am fairly confident that this is a zebra crossing because of the black and white stripes painted on the tarmac. There are no buttons, and no traffic lights for the motorists; but there are two yellow spherical beacons on either side, each of them on a tall black post which like the tarmac also has white stripes, in this case wrapped around it.

The beacons blink, or flash, all day and all night, but they do so out of phase: thinking about it, I didn't before living next to such a crossing have any assumption either way as to whether the two beacons which bookend it are on the same electrical circuit or not; but the fact that these two blink out of phase makes me think it is unlikely. One of them has a regular blink, by which I mean it is on for about the same time it is off, and this goes at about 80 beats per minute; the one on the other side (and this is the best I can do) seems on for 4 beats and off for 3, those beats being fast, something like 230 per minute. Together they make me think sometimes of Ferneyhough and sometimes of Chopin.

It might be possible, by noting the moment at which both lights switch on simultaneously, and then counting first only one of them, and then only the other, until they are simultaneous again, to figure out the phase pattern they are in. Maybe they will be in a ratio of one prime against the nearest, like 19:23. I have thought about doing this for more than a year but have never been in the mood. There would be no point in trying to figure it out from the individual on/off timings; the tiniest error in the beats-per-minute (and those given here are very approximate) would become enormous.

Enough about the beacons. They are trouble: especially given the fact that there is, actually, another zebra crossing immediately adjoined to the one I can see, which means that even if I did figure out the phase pattern of these two beacons, there would only be opened up the whole new nightmare of figuring out how they relate to the phase of the third beacon, on the second crossing, which is not only also very much out of phase with the first two, but is not even visible from my window, so that in order to make any headway whatsoever I'd have to make all the necessary observations outside and in the cold.

For the last time, enough about the beacons. The best thing about the crossing is, obviously, the way people are. Some people, in order to thank a motorist for stopping for them, raise their eyebrows, tilt their head downwards, and their flattened hand (fingers together) upwards at about 30 degrees toward the car. Others lean far further forward with both their eyebrows and their hands raised even further; and you could be forgiven for theorizing that the grander the salute, the more people lean into it in order to make it. As the angle of the arm goes toward 45 degrees it becomes much more likely that the palm of the hand will be vertical, and that the angle at the wrist is therefore sharper. Of course, some people completely ignore the motorist and walk over the crossing: either genuinely oblivious, wanderingly, maybe lost to whatever is playing through their headphones, or, when their ignoring the motorist is more awkward and studied, they walk across with their eyes fixed somewhere in the distance in front of them.

If people doing gestures of thanks is good, the gestures people make when cars fail to stop for them is even better. I don't know for sure the legality of it, but I remember once being told: if you are just standing on the kerb, however expectant or purposeful you look, no vehicle is under any obligation to stop for you. If however you have so much as one foot on the tarmac of the crossing itself, then they must. I have seen cars tear across this crossing without stopping even when people are almost a yard into the road; and definitely on one occasion there was very nearly a nasty accident.

Predictably some people react angrily. I have noticed this getting worse over the year, and maybe, just maybe, it is to do with the fact that of the five white stripes painted on the road, only one is intact: two have worn away almost completely, the central one eroded so that it looks weirdly like a bone, and another is visible but a mess.

When a driver doesn't stop for someone, the response is sometimes quite spectacular. Men who are about fifty often fling both their hands into the air, fingers splayed, mouth wide open, and rotate themselves, usually left-right-left or right-left-right, slowing down in either case, and the one or the other depending on, well, we can't know; but certainly once the car has torn past their attention immediately shifts from it and focuses on the surroundings, the pavements, as if they want to survey immediately for any other witness who is as outraged as they are, so they might raise eyebrows at each other in solidarity.

Best of all are the docile but clearly immensely powerful warlocks, usually younger, slighter men, nearer to thirty, who—once they have expressed being put out at a car not stopping for them by way of a very gentle jolt, and with very slightly raised eyebrows—absolutely and on the contrary do not shift their focus from the car. Their lips will purse, subtly, but with immense meaning, and they will turn their body to fix their eyes on the back of the car, as if by intently staring at the rear number-plate they are laying a permanent hex on its registrant. It all seems a very private act, certainly not for the benefit of the motorist—no such gesture could, the pedestrian always out of the motorists' field of view in an instant—but neither, unlike the more spectacular gestures, does it seem to be behaviour which hopes for an audience.

16 Beyond the top field

There was an old man who lived just outside of a village, near to where I grew up. The village which he lived just outside of was extremely thin and extremely long, being at the bottom of a valley with a river running through it, and it was named 'Roadwater' after its primary constituents. I met the old man maybe once. I knew his son, who worked at the garage, and who called me 'Tiger Tim'. I don't know what the old man did. Perhaps he was retired. Or maybe he had done a job from some other era, and had found himself getting less and less work. What he was famous for was his tea. It was generally advised in hushed tones that you were to be wary of it, or at least to take it seriously.

The story was that he would wake each day, at some extravagantly early hour, as ancient people can drift into doing, and would then set simmering a pan of water with between six and ten teabags in it. Every now and again, he would top it up with more hot water, and perhaps sometimes take it off the heat, but by the afternoon—as every man and woman and child knew—it was stewed beyond any tea you had heretofore encountered, or even imagined. Every mouthful, it was said, was like drinking a sweaty saddle. You could pour it out, wait for it to ooze into taking the shape of the tray, and then cut it into chunks, in the manner of a flapjack. Each of those would usually be sold to local barbers and hung on the wall, where it would be used as a razor strop. Occasionally parts of it would coalesce around a single point, perhaps a small piece of grit. They tended to form fairly sharp but formidably dense little cones; these were sent to the farrier, who used them a little like nails or tacks, to hold horseshoes temporarily in place on hooves. I held one in my hand for a few minutes; I remember that its weight was intolerable and that after it was removed, the feeling of oppressiveness remained. Telling this now I find myself wondering what colour the old man's teeth were. Whether the glow they gave off was even within the visible spectrum.

The old man's tea, without milk, was not really a drink at all. Bring your own milk, people whispered, and mix it in. If you don't want to be able to chew it. The insides of the old man's cups had built up such layers of dark brown over the years that they seemed to subtract light from the room.

Once a year the river would run murky, all deep reds and browns, and people from the village would always say something about the hills being so iron-rich. In truth, we knew the old man had got up even earlier than usual, having had an instinct that there would be a fall of heavy rain, and had emptied his teabag bin into the waterfall beyond the top field.

17 Solstice

One winter night I was thirteen or so the western sky was pulsing as a golden land two starlings broke from flock and died above me their circlings wobbled to a single falling and like twigs three skeletons dropped not a feather on them to the beach. From two dead birds the artefacts of three between them four eye-sockets cleanly empty I saw the other two blaze a moment then harden through into deep obsidian gaps five seconds after this the birds were ash six seconds after they were gone.

The sky was pulsing as a golden land I was thirteen or so and all around me twenty-one ambassadors held in visit from some richer world than ours spaced in perfect measures on the beach fourteen shadows seven fire-ghosts seven bonfires and this exact on sunset. So were the light and dark both split apart and bound.

18 Raindrops

Near Seven Dials in Brighton there is a lamp-post on a corner which is a different shape from the others. Perhaps it is older. There is more gold to its light, possibly indicating that it burns different chemicals, or even that it runs off different electricity.

If you watch it in the dark, when it is raining heavily, rain water collects immediately underneath the light, hanging there in droplets. These droplets become larger and larger until they are too heavy to be held there, and fall to the ground.

But while they are becoming larger they collect and reflect inside them the golden light from the lamp, and they glow. When they drop under their own weight they string out into fragments, which too catch glints of the light from the lamp above, before becoming invisible again, or at least the same dark as the rest. Perhaps they recall at this point comets breaking up in an atmosphere, viewed from beneath, into the same dark as the rest.

From a distance it looks like the lamp is a small raised furnace or kiln, in a container attached to a tall pole, which must be occasionally leaking, in bright drips of molten metal, like time-lapsed footage of fruit growing. These drips probably then enter into a different spectrum of light as they drop and cool, one less visible.

If you look at it for a while it is possible to imagine a stalagmite of metal forming on the pavement underneath the lamp. I don't think one exists, but this is not just because it is still, as I've mentioned, raining heavily. It's likely that this rain would either help to cool the metal as it formed a mound, or would have even less effect, simply vanishing into a dying frond of steam.

There is no steam to be seen, in any case. One possible conclusion is that the substance dripping from the lamp is some sort of replacement for the material of the pavement, which melts a small amount of pavement as it lands—an amount exactly in proportion with the size of the drip. So that in the end, everything ends up just as it was, and the surface is neither pocked nor mounded.

As I have mentioned, it is raining heavily, and this perhaps helps to smooth over the surface of the replaced pavement. But not too smooth, otherwise people would notice. The lamp is switched off in the daytime, likely for this reason too. Why the pavement needs replacing in this manner isn't something I've been able to discover.

19 A curse

Walking along the canal with a small black carrier bag, just tobacco and milk and the paper, and practising aloud the replies I wished I'd made to the shopkeeper, I stumbled into a triangulation. It felt accidental, but could not have been. It was alarming, a beautiful summer's afternoon suddenly host to a splinter of insanity, over which I had no choice. In the space of half a second I noticed one bent-down spike among a thicket of spikes, a wrong plant, and the reflection of a chimney in the water. The thicket of spikes was of the kind fitted to deter birds, the plant was growing from the wall, and was deformed, its stems had grown as sinewy flat ribbons when they should have been dainty and twiglike, and the chimney was an incinerator which seemed always to be in the middle distance of the city. It looked like a huge cigarette. It wobbled in the water as gunk and froth glid past it on the surface. These three things together were markers, they stopped me dead still. I felt I was more than merely noticing, more even than looking or staring, but still not comprehending.

Maybe I *was* comprehending, that was my next thought. My body grew tense and I felt excited, fretful. It was nothing to do with the three objects themselves.

A sigil had been pulled taut between them, but they lent none of their specific individual lives to its meaning. This taut sigil, I realised now, was just for me. Its meaning exponentiated like a scream. I was so angry that I had no other thoughts. To be myself was a crashing tide of rage. I was imagining torture and murder. My soul in seconds had become incandescent with the memory of someone cruel, someone who had harmed me without shame or regret or apology, and my consciousness was flooded with a simple question. Would I curse him: yes or no.

I ran. Bolted, along the towpath. I ran for at least three minutes, until at last some other thoughts came back to me. Something other than anger and retaliation. I had never thought to curse anyone in my life. Walking slowly back home, I tried to put it from my mind, but I failed. Turning the key to lock my front door, I realised, taking my shoes off, thinking of the chimney's reflection, that I hadn't given an answer.

M

In the middle of the night I understood a face. It was above the bed, a few inches above my head. I had been sleeping on my side, my own face pushed into the pillow. The face I suddenly understood was upright and in the air. I was asleep, and then I knew it was there; it was my knowing it was there that woke me. I could not see it. Opening my eyes made no difference to what I could or could not see. The curtains were drawn, the lights were off. In the pitch black I knew I couldn't see the face. The dark got everywhere, being in the dark was total, it changed my sight the way being deep under the surface of the ocean changes hearing. I knew that even if the lights had been on, I still couldn't have seen the face, and I knew I couldn't touch it. I knew where it was, and which way it was staring. I knew how dangerous it was, and I knew not to move. I knew that I didn't understand where it was from, and knew I was scared of where it was from almost as much as I was scared of the face itself. It wasn't looking at me, it wasn't looking at anything, but I knew it had me in mind, as I had it in mind. I was no more or less real to it than it was to me.

Knowing all this, without knowing how I knew it, without even questioning how, I wondered if the face could see me, or could touch me. Not that it mattered, since I knew more than anything else not to move, and that was so important it was tamping down other thoughts. Could it hear me, and would it speak to me. If it did speak, would it be in a language I could understand. I understood the presence of a face which I couldn't see or touch, maybe I could understand other things too. None of it of any consequence. I simply knew not to move. I did not move. I was still for I don't know how long. The face neither willed me nor reacted as I waded into Lethe, it just watched the room. I knew it would not move, either.

The shock of being jolted from sleep, and my eyes were open again. How brief the sleep was I've no idea, but it had been deep and spacious. As deep and spacious a sleep as my sudden wakefulness now was sharp and clear, even more than my first waking, when I'd known the face was there. I saw almost the same darkness as before. Not absolute now, there was a patch of grey light on the curtain, so some time must have passed, but too dark to make out anything in the room. The face was gone, I knew it was gone as surely as I'd known it was there. I felt very alone, very aware of the channels of empty space either side of my bed, as if knowing they were empty somehow made them suddenly frightening. Anything could be there. Only nothing was. The face was gone. I can't describe it to you because it did not exist visually. It didn't look like anything. I understood it the way I would understand a human face, yet without understanding what kind of creature it belonged to. The memory was vanishing like a dream, and I was already asking myself, how could I recognise and understand a face which had no features. It wasn't there. From inches above my head came two voices at once:

—You want help.

—You want it to hurt.

I sat up, wrapping myself to my throat in the duvet. It had been the same voice, coming from separate mouths, simultaneously. The face, which was gone, could speak different things at the same time. There was no doubt it was the face had spoken. The words were awkward but definite, as if the mouths were proficient but not practised in this language. The mouths, my ears told me, had been in the exact same place as each other, and in the exact same place as the face had been. These were not questions it was asking me; they were statements, or perhaps threats. They had been delivered in an inhumanly loud whisper, as if organically amplified and ripped out from some hollowness, the resonance of a thin but tall room, a space which couldn't possibly exist in the air just inches above my bed.

After a few seconds, somewhere in front of me, across vast space, and through an echo the size of a car park or a cathedral, I heard, I don't know what I heard. Was it a small lid being replaced, perhaps, or a light coin being placed on a saucer. The echo faded, the way they do, and the walls of my room were real again. Perhaps the echo I had heard was that under a canal bridge. I pulled up a pillow so that I could lean, upright still but slightly sideways, and I slumped motionless, in a silence at last of the right size again. The shape of my room.

I knew that I was deep under the surface of consequences, and I knew I couldn't stop what was already happening, that I was already changed, but I thought I might be able to stay alert to it. In other words I knew not to fall asleep, and I did not fall asleep. I was understanding the face more and more. The danger of it. I was frightened, having now heard it, that if I closed my eyes, I might see it. I knew that even though I had heard its voice twice in the same moment, it was only one. This face, which I was so frightened of seeing that I couldn't close my eyes, was only one face. After forever came dawn, and my room was made soft with grey light.

M

The deformed plant with the flat stems is gone from the wall along the towpath. I know this not just because it is winter now but because the bent-down spike and the reflection of the incinerator chimney now form a triangle with me as the third point. The plant does not matter now. They follow me in my thoughts. Often I imagine that I will jump into the canal. It is like a recurring dream, but it happens when I am awake. It happens when I am awake because I no longer feel the need to sleep. In the waking dream I stare at the reflection of the incinerator and I become convinced that if I dive into the canal correctly I can smack my head on the rim of the chimney and crack my skull open. As if the chimney will somehow be there in the canal, beneath the surface, in place of its reflection. In reality the chimney is probably five times as wide as the canal. Every time I jump into the canal in my imagination I gore my right eye out on the bent-down spike. I am still angry. Sometimes I think of tying the man who hurt me to a chair and slowly pouring the contents of a boiled kettle over him. Sometimes I think of attacking his face with a hammer. Or simply knifing him in the abdomen from behind. Sometimes I remember the face in the night, and its voices. I try to picture it and I cannot. What I am sure of is that it was not a ghost. I have never used, aloud, the name I want to give it, and I won't write it here, because I am frightened that to identify it correctly might energize it, somehow. I try not to think about it at all, but I fail.

M

I am in bed on Sunday afternoon. I have just had sex with my favourite hookup, and the daydream is back with me as he snores. He is twenty-four, and somehow effortlessly built, a nice hung boy who studies languages at university and responds to compliments with the guile and deftness of a penguin, apparently keeping all his poise and confidence in reserve for sex. We are seeing more and more of each other, becoming friends even, and now he is curled up placid as a fox and facing away from me. It is a good and a nourishing thing when, in the presence of someone kind, anger at past harm begins to feel tinctured the way memories are, as if one day memory is all the anger might be. This daydream of the sigil, or the curse, is again in my mind, though, and I see the gentle movement of the canal water, the chimney reflection undulates, I imagine it solid and real under the surface, I imagine smacking my head against its concrete, so that my face is mashed into it, my lips tearing, my front teeth beginning to chip and crack, and my alarming blood curling out into the dirty brown water. I am aware constantly of the bent-down spike which will pierce and ruin one of my eyes if I do jump in. For the first time, I think, what if that eye doesn't matter.

Something is different. I feel strange, lighter, as if a new idea of who I am, or what I am, has landed on me, settled in me, from nowhere. It feels like removing a spider-web, having walked into one. I know what I want. Staring at the back of someone's beautiful neck as he slumbers, I know what I want. The person who hurt me is already cursed, he cursed himself when he did what he did. He deserves what he deserves. They must have been questions after all. I don't know what they mean, but I know how they are to be answered. Do I want help. Go on then. Do I want it to hurt.

I know what I am going to do, and somehow I know what the immediate consequences will be. So I wrap my arms awkwardly around this young man. I know he will appreciate it. I pull the duvet tight, round the two of us, and to both questions I offer the answer: yes. I barely make a sound, but my mouth shapes the word distinctly, deliberately. I feel as if I am speaking this answer twice, simultaneously.

He makes a noise as the chill wakes him up. What the fuck, he seems to say. The room became so cold, the instant I said 'yes', that the windows immediately misted up, and just seconds later droplets are trickling down them. He snuggles even tighter inside the duvet, obviously not to be dragged from his gorgeous rest without considerable protest. I know to wait. I wonder whether I will ever see what is happening, or is going to happen. Who or what I have said yes to. I know it will be worse than mere boiling water, worse than anything I could come up with myself. Whatever it is, it's deserved. I decide that I will walk by the canal, later. For now, I will hug this beautiful boy. What's happening is already happening.

20 Corralie Lyon

Once, in the caff, a jowly old man who seemed lost in his own little world suddenly gathered himself. He looked a little unwashed, like he didn't cope very well. He downed the last of his mug of tea, as if in tremendous need of its fortifying powers, put on his heavy coat, and slung his bag over his shoulder. He stood up, and grandly cleared his throat, as if to address the whole room. My boyfriend and I were at the very next table, very hungover, and we prepared ourselves for something unusual. The woman behind the counter saw what was going on, but did not seem too concerned.

The jowly old man had an unexpectedly commanding presence. The caff fell silent, which he visibly waited for. Then, he said, to everyone:

—Some of you will have known Corralie Lyon.

(Absolute silence.)

—She died on Friday, at her own hand.

The jowly old man solemnly walked out of the caff. He crossed over, to Mr Khachatari's. I looked at my boyfriend, then looked back outside. The old man was nowhere to be seen. There was a rustle, generally, of clothing and objects, as everyone returned to their food, and there was a murmur of voices, one of incomprehension, similar from every table. A loud hiss from a coffee machine made me jump, and I felt sick, for a few seconds. It seemed to be the case that not one person in the caff had known Corralie Lyon.

Finishing our breakfast, my boyfriend and I wondered: Why did he say 'at'? Wasn't the phrase '*by* one's own hand'? We noticed that the jowly old man had left his newspapers on the table, and remembered that before his announcement he had been writing, quite intently, in biro. My boyfriend stood, warm and quick and gorgeous in his hangover, and stretched over to the jowly old man's table. He grabbed the mess of newspaper, and I shoved our mugs and plates closer to the wall so as to make room. He put the jowly old man's newspaper down on our table, and spread it flat. It was the Express. We began to leaf through it.

All the margins, every span of free space to be found, was full of chaotic scribbles. Not one word, just loose zigzags—everywhere, going on and on and on, overlapping each other, and seemingly slipping off the paper's edge at points. Presumably that's what the dark flecks on the man's table had been, the occasional quiet tapping.

21 The crow, again

There is something to be said about distant buildings distinct on the skyline which, when kept in sight and walked toward, seem never to get any closer, and toward which there seems to be no direct route, and whose curious inaccessibility would certainly remain, even if you were suddenly spirited into the body of a crow, capable of taking unimpeded that shortest route between two points for which your new form is, perhaps a little arbitrarily, the unelected and oblivious ambassador.

Whatever it is that's to be said about these buildings, it is either right now inaccessible or unapproachable to me, much like the buildings themselves, or, it is as simple as just pointing out that they exist, much as the buildings themselves do.

22 Every ended soul

Seen from the plane window what must be called the clouds seem in what must be relative close-up still distinct only in what must nevertheless be their immense distance from you and are by the look of them implausibly, unreasonably still, they hang like something deeply familiar whose capacity for change or persistence through time has suddenly been locked down, unscalable terrains in every aspect a simulation of suspense, they are total and between and are a section, they are ideal and romantic, they are a blueprint of what you could rolling out to the horizons expand and see should you having cracked a single moment open and into it poured an infinity felt yourself too fall in and brighten through in sympathy, the layers stretch as far as they can and slightly more gold, and perhaps in each of these individual ecstatic interims, each infinity of vapour cliffs and vapour islands hanging still between blinding white layers screened off from sun and land, perhaps in each of these newly minted images of a world, every ended soul, from a sparrow to a god, is billowing by billowing and frond by frond memorialized, but it seems less than likely.

23 Click

The word 'forensic' goes back to the middle of the 17th century. It's from the Latin 'forensis', meaning 'in open court, or 'public', which itself comes from 'forum'.

I remember being a little surprised to learn this. It's a fine tilt away from that usage you find—especially in the humanities, I suppose—where it seems more often to point to an exactness of process, or to a foregrounding of those investigations which take place on finer scales. You know, how a deep close-reading of a text may be called 'forensic'.

That slight difference between how the word is deployed now, and its origins, conjures a vivid zoom or blur effect in my mind, a movement which I can see, can feel, and which somehow has an audible click to it.

It's like this: imagine viewing a theatre, from above, via some lensed device, and changing the focus of that device such that the seats encircling the theatre all vanish into a blur, and the centre becomes more and more prominent, until all that's in focus—such sharp focus—is the vicious little instrument at the centre of everything, quivering in some physician's hand, along with the layers of tissue it's peeling apart.

It feels like it is subject to a subtle recalibration, as if what is adjusted about the word 'forensic' between these two usages is its focal length—its intensity of attention moved as if concentrically from the fact of something being done in public to the fact that it is being dissected.

24 Resurrection

As I was walking back from town, I rounded the corner of the Salvation Army Church, from Union Road into Park Crescent, when I saw a man in front of me. I'd say three yards ahead, facing me, arms folded, stood still. His right side was close up to the building; he was very much on that side of the pavement, almost as if avoiding a steady stream of absent pedestrians going in the other direction.

He looked to be about sixty, and was a fantastic shape: a very round, bald head, with freckles and liver spots, and he was stocky, and all of a foot shorter than me. I could not and still cannot figure out what it was that his shape reminded me of. Some sort of formal hat probably would have been appropriate.

I'm fairly sure I didn't jump, even though he took me by surprise. Perhaps I inhaled sharply. He was, to begin with, absolutely motionless, except that after I rounded the corner fully we briefly made eye contact, whereupon he immediately started walking. In that moment, the eye contact, there was a barely-visible click went through him, the tiniest recalibration of everything—and then another, a bit like a delicate nod of assent, the engine of a butler starting. After these two extraordinarily subtle resets to his being, and looking no longer at me but purposefully ahead, he began walking.

As we walked past each other I had an extreme sense that something deeply uncanny and wrong was happening. This increased to overwhelming intensity, almost like a sound or a scream inside my head, across the space of just a second or two, so I turned around in alarm. There was no sign of him. I darted back to the corner. He simply couldn't have gone anywhere: there was nowhere to vanish to.

Even while turning around, I felt that my image of him in memory was crumbling, falling apart into very oblique strokes—bold circles and whooshing rhombuses, like a diagram of a man mid-activity, or a box of postcards dropped in a strong wind. As my image of him had scattered itself to nothing, so his physical form had vanished too.

The rest of the way home I found myself wondering if I'd wandered accidentally into a spell, or a ceremony; wondering even whether this perturbing event was, itself, a hex being laid on me. Optimistically, I thought to myself: perhaps if he was a wizard, he was a good one; if a ghost, hopefully benevolent.

That night, I accepted that he had been neither of those things. He was far too unsettling and far too fleshly. In those two subtle clicks he had changed, I believe, from dead to alive; and, for whatever reason, he had then changed to something else altogether, too fast for me to see it happen. I didn't sleep.

25 Doors, walls

Have you ever imagined your house with every door open? You could go and open them all, for real, but even then, it would be hard to see them all open at once. So imagine them all open, all at once. Wide open, as far as possible, however open they can be, against whatever first stops them from rotating any further. That version of your house, with all of its doors as open as they can be, is what a ghost wanders about in.

It's obviously never been the case that they can walk through doors, any more than we can. It's just—much less magically, I'm afraid to say—that ghosts exist in a reality where all doors are as open as they can be, for all of time. An aggregate reality of all possible open doors.

The idea that they can somehow pass through a slab of wood seems almost silly. Who or what can do that? If you ever notice a ghost seeming to pass through a door, you're really looking at a ghost walking through the gap made by an opened door. The fact that the door, to you, is closed, is neither here nor there. It's not that it merely looks closed, or seems closed; there's no trickery. In our world, the door is closed.

Maybe ghosts exist in a world where you actually can't shut doors, and maybe sometimes they might even prefer to, if they had the choice. Who knows. But the nearest closed door to you—look at it—is wide open, to a ghost. And it even looks like it's wide open, to a ghost, as vividly as it looks shut to you.

All the doors in your house, wide open, all at once. That's the first step. If you want to get a clearer sense of what it is that ghosts wander about in, you ought really to imagine every building you're familiar with, every one you can remember, with all of its doors as wide-open as they can be.

Doors are a simple case. We must now apply a similar logic to walls. There is a sense in which talk of ghosts existing 'in other dimensions' is literally true, if a little banal.

We can simplify our mental model of a door such that it is simply a section of a wall which opens and closes. *Opening* and *closing* just mean a partial rotation back and forth about an axis: one of its edges, the edge where the hinges are. It's a folding-out from a wall, in dimensions familiar to us, which leaves a gap. Let's hold on to that, as our idea of opening a door.

A wall is a shape with edges. Whatever a door is to a wall, so a wall is to the plane on which it lies. Just as ghosts can't actually pass through doors, but seem to, because they exist in a reality where all doors are open, ghosts cannot actually pass through walls either: they merely seem to, because they exist in a reality where all are walls are open, every single one, hinged along an edge into a dimension which we can scarcely comprehend. It is for the reasons given here, as well as certain other reasons, that many corners are haunted.

If you happen to live in a lighthouse, you may have an even harder time.

Imagine your house with every single door open. Imagine your house with every single wall open, too. Folded out, and lying along some other plane, perhaps not even visible in the imagination. That's correct, that's how it is.

26 The mock suns

I am hugging tightly down on a high ledge, six feet by three, the long edge attached; it's covered by a piece of flat lead, bent smoothly at the edges and folded at the corners as if with ease. It is not raining: the city is sandstone down below and the sky is bright clear blue, host to a dry heat not yet uncomfortable.

My ledge must be something to do with the drainage of some terrifyingly high part of a roof, almost never accessed, as it is covered with a constantly-running glaze of beautiful water, which I would be drinking were I not concerned about the lead content—I feel perhaps this water has been flowing down from hundreds upon hundreds of even higher lead-coated ledges, in some spire of this building which pushes up above me forever into the sky.

I am naked in the heat except for a baseball cap worn backwards which has been gifted me and which I feel is not something I would usually wear. And nor is this how I would wear it if I did. But I look cute. I feel like I want to be fucked. I daren't look, any twisting round of my body is perilous and I may fall down to what is beneath, an image of which I cannot quite commit to memory, even though every time I flatten myself completely down onto the ledge—why do I not get wet?—I glimpse through the bright waterfall what may be gardens beneath.

Each sun in the sky—there are three—is black. The sky is bright, yet I see the halos. Each sun resembles at once an eclipse and a large round hole punched from a piece of blue paper, or a drastic computer-graphic deletion. Each circular gap, each black sun, seems to be subtly sliding up and down. Their paths are not curved, but are simply a straight line. The three gaps of sun with their halos slide up and down as if representing configurations of something unseen, or readings on some monitor.

I heave myself back up onto the ledge, crouching. I hold on, shaking, to a pipe sticking from a wall. On a nearby ledge to my left, a crouched man's spine audibly snaps, and sticks out from the back of him pointing to the sky: he buries his face in the leaded water, draws his thighs in, pushing his protruding spine out at an even more alarming angle. I watch the root of his pelvis, dragged up by his abdominal muscles, reattach to his skeleton somewhere around the ribcage. Across the angle created between his old and new spines, a webbing, a thick shelf of bone grows. Dark blue spiders, the size of rabbits, with deformed, fatty, distended legs, pour down it. Soon I am being fucked by the first in a line of men I do not recognize who are wearing motor racing gear. There is a stink of weed which I don't want to smoke.

27 Three of us

Someone yelled my name, in alarm, from something like fifty yards away. I heard it echoing round the street, except that I was in my room, and it came from a direction where there is a wall. There wasn't an open window, or anything like one. There are no windows in that direction, no doors, no vents; and besides, the sound wasn't a shout heard through an aperture, it was a shout heard outside. I remember that night thinking that yelling my name in alarm was very likely a trick. I didn't sleep.

That was years ago. More recently, one night, a year into total isolation and absolutely drunk, I stared out of the window at an empty can rolling about in the strong wind. I decided it was alive, and decided that the very fact I was watching it was something alive too, an entity in itself, a third living thing. It was a consciousness I had no control over, because the can was behaving as it wanted, and it was a consciousness the can had no control over, because I was able to shut down the watching at will; and so the watching or the watchfulness was separate from the can and separate from me, responsive to both of us. There were three of us.

Later that night it seemed to me that rain was proof of gravity, and that this was somehow exemplary, and was something that might save me from losing my mind. I remember pleading with the universe that something else must exist too, something singular and plural, in the way that rain is singular and plural, and that this thing made of things be proof of something, too, proof of something that I desperately needed. I was unable to guess what it was that I desperately needed, but it seemed to me that sufficient proof of it would be something I could only call 'angels'. They would be nothing like the angels you get in religion. Angels would arrive the way rain arrives, and would be just as tactile, and just as vast and just as detailed; and they would be proof of something, the way rain was proof of gravity.

When I opened the window, much later, the can was gone. The winds had died down. Outside was silent. I missed the company of the can, dancing around the tarmac, and I missed the company of the third entity we had generated together, which perhaps was also proof of something. With the window shut, and an old bedsheet hung from nails in the frame to block out the light of the beacons, since I had no blind or curtain yet, I closed my eyes and transmitted a silent scream, a hailing, to that third entity, having some sense now of what to call it.

28 He lies buried

The very last sentence of *Daniel Orme* by Herman Melville, which is also its entire last paragraph, has no commas in it, and none of the other punctuation marks either. It is beautiful and strange:

> He lies buried among other sailors for whom also strangers performed the last rites in a lonely plot overgrown with wild eglantine uncared for by man.

The entire text of *Daniel Orme* is only four or five pages long. This final sentence begins with a simple statement after which without any typographical indicators of pause or of syntax there follow successive fronds of inevitable detail.

The sentence as with all others must be encountered through time, as in, it takes time, which is not reversible, to read each word, in the order they appear—but once the full stop has been reached the sentence seems to me to collapse the time it took to read it; it has the sense of being a singular thought, an entire and intact image which, despite being such an image, complete and instantaneous, cannot but be expressed in a sentence which has duration, has extent both in time and on the page.

It strikes me as the kind of sentence, paragraph—whole image—which in another language might be expressed in a single long word, the many morphemes all inflecting and re-shaping each other, the way tree-roots grow through and around themselves, in vegetable chaos: an entity of internal loopings and self-modifications. Yet it also feels more unstable and quantum than that; you can stare back at this sentence while its different parts seem simultaneously to affect each other differently, like a shimmering entity of shifting mirrors.

What seems at first sight to be a mere absence of commas ramifies out and becomes the presence of an ambiguity, a kind of twilit, pulsing ambiguity which itself seems to have living structure, an ambiguity whose symmetries and contradictions glint as the light changes around it—as your imagination illuminates it differently. Mine took its metaphorical cue from the fact that *Daniel Orme* is the story of an ending, and I imagined his burial-plot, just as much as his death—which precedes his being

> discovered alone and dead on a height overlooking the seaward sweep of the great haven to whose shore, in his retirement from sea, he had moored

—at dusk. This description of the discovery of Daniel Orme's body is almost unpunctuated, is almost yet another succession of fronds of inevitable detail. But there are commas, still; and those markers of syntax, those invitations to vocal pauses, or both, keep this sentence firmly moored in the realm of prose. The commas seem to mark time like buoys in an ocean. It reminds us that we are reading it.

Yet the ending seems to succeed in being outside of time. The image contained in this very last sentence, the very end of the last thing Melville lived to finish, does not really feel like its home cosmos is prose at all: it is more like seeing something than reading something. It has the integrity of a singular and final thought, a moment encouraged strangely out into prose along an unbroken line, with the fluency of calligraphic brushwork, like the streak left on a calm sea or calm sky in the wake of a vessel.

29 Like deep water

Against the imagined black sky of starless sea feel your unmoving body drift as an arched mandala out into concavity and convexity at once, and that heaviness of undulation from first eyelids as a seeable surface to the dark unseeable black as a pooling absolute of foreground without focus and background without focus and all the empty distances without focus in between, then again the inward of the eyelids as a seeable surface, then again the dark unseeable black as a pooling absolute of once-blue foreground without focus and once-blue background without focus and all the empty darkening distances without focus in between, and in a yawn of fully opened focus into which the whole sea hears itself pour the ears open inward gaps down to the jaw, and your pooling outward underwater sounds more like underwater than it does to something starless, and memories as inward textured wax irrupting, sliding on the surface of dark absences will pool about as well, the vivid mixing sinks into itself and against a visible black starless sky of visible black starless sea you feel your unmoving body or the attributes it so far above once had drift as an arched mandala out into felt, responsive concavity and felt, responsive convexity at once, and the unresponsive substance in the wax circles meets and joins above like screensavers on a pooling newly-convex sea-monitor the curved width of something starless, and response and felt substance and the memory of attribution generally all slide like sea over through each other and disconnect like deep water in pulpy threads and reattach, qualities and singular things melt likewise into fingers and are pulled apart at the fringes to a pool of sleep, a single inward this time full of verticals and trees in silhouette and lamplight, some dream set in Craven Woods at night, below the Whitehawk mast, the place you know so well, while simultaneously somewhere you have never been.

30 The dragon

Smoking a cigarette in B and F's garden the other night—I had nipped out alone—I looked west at the night sky and I saw, thought I saw—it was facing, eventually, the sea—a great roaring dragon of cloud, drawn out in grey on darker grey, deep leadlike charcoal on rich slate. It had a muscular neck, an imperious eye with a domed brow, and its jaws—god help any creature it chose to bite down on—its jaws were—wait—its jaws were creaking slowly apart still—but this isn't a roar, this isn't threatening, this is—and I found myself—and I found it absurd as I noticed I was doing it—*yawning*: doing so in reflex sympathy, and then in warm empathy, with a tired old dragon made of clouds. His yawn melted out into the sky as he did, jaws patched transparent and indistinct by the wrapping sky, all drifting outward to nothing but slowly northward, so slowly northward, surely creaking as they did so, drifting to nothing—or drifting, perhaps, to sleep. In a snug dragon nest, it is to be hoped. Rrraaaaawwn.

31 A crop circle

Look out at the channel, from Brighton. When it is dark, a shallow constellation of powerful red lights, each installed on a spoke of the offshore windfarm—like warning dew gently resting on top of it—blinks 'W' in Morse code, through until morning. I have never been watching it when those lights go off. One evening, I thought I would try to watch for the moment they all turned on, and was surprised to find that they do not all come on at the same time.

R and E took us quite close to the windfarm the last time we took K's boat out. It's an eerie, beautiful structure, always doing strange things with scale. Completely impossible in the water to tell how far away you are from any individual pillar, until you are right up close to one. The way those individual pillars form into different lines stretching away from you as you walk, slowly, along the seafront, recalls the precipitously redrawn angles seen when travelling on a train past anything planted in a grid. Apple trees, vineyards.

It might be worthwhile to find out the shape of the grid the windfarm makes, then take a boat out one night, with a big rope, and tie an elaborate pattern or knot—or, perhaps, not even bother with the rope: just sail a sigil round the windfarm, carving it into water which loses it in an instant, like trying to stamp a crop circle in plants which won't be flattened, and trust the sea that what it wants to remember it will remember.

JETSAM

32 Mound

Menacing on the bed of whatever catastrophe of contoured gridiron embers was left after some clattering ghast had gone over the milky scum in a coracle and pumped it away to shore there remained too a sinister pillow, awaiting the weary traveller, a soft mound of snapped birds, all jabbing spitefully with the only movement they had left, which was except in a few cases a slight raising of their left wingtip. They did this as frequently as they could, which was not very frequently, and it came to resemble a coordinated pulsing, which was unfortunate, not just because these desperate gestures simulated in wondrous concert community, where there was not even hope, but also because the mound looked from a chain away as if it were itself breathing.

Another sorrowful result was that the mound slowly shook itself, like a packet of crisps, with the smaller birds being sifted to the bottom of the mound where they were under the sheer weight of the rest of the mound even more comprehensively snapped. It should be noted that at no point did a bird, having been snapped, separate: a mercy, perhaps, as this would have caused each half to be sifted downward further still, and perhaps mistaken by a smaller bird for company.

The trees nearby were beautiful, the clouds were gentle; the trees knew nothing, but the clouds had access to the controls of a heated metal plate underneath the mound which although its purpose was unclear certainly had a number of discernible effects. The sharp winter air was well-received.

I'm going to tell you more about this, when I am having a better day, whether you like it or not. In particular, about the substance produced at the bottom of the mound when the clouds raised the temperature of the heated plate sufficiently; its aromas; whether it was summer or winter; whether the clouds were acting on their own behalf or as a proxy; that they were in fact acting as a proxy, on behalf of another proxy; who or what this secondary proxy was; what its individual motives were; who that proxy was itself acting on behalf of, further motives, and so on.

33 At the very bottom of a cave there was nobody

It was a long, low cave, damp and foul and strewn with eyeless creatures. The creatures were like oily flatbreads, or elongated, crimped kombucha. They did not slither over each other but kept a small distance apart, so that in certain light it looked as if the cave floor was dotted with puddles of foul brown water.

These creatures lived for many years, and only in this one place, a place nobody had ever been able to find, or to travel to on purpose, but a place where unhappy travellers had nevertheless sometimes found themselves. Before I travelled here, I would have said I was unhappy, but happiness and unhappiness alike seemed both to be meaningless after just a few minutes awake in this company.

The creatures communicated with each other by tapping thin wooden rods onto the ground. In terms of our own senses they neither saw nor heard. It is likely they did not smell or taste, either. Each creature was able to hold fifteen, sixteen, or seventeen rods.

I do not know what to call the extremities by which a rod was held. They were small tendrils just proud of the edge, and those which were functional were able to curl enough to hold a small rod. They vaguely recalled the eyes of clams: a constellation or beading of uncanny little limblets, dotted round the rim like molten sentries.

The creatures had no obvious symmetry to them, but each looked as if it somehow ought to have grown with eighteen such tendrils, capable therefore of holding eighteen rods. Those with only fifteen rod-holding parts, for instance, had three outgrowths which had not developed to functionality.

Each of the rods by which the creatures communicated might have been a satire of cheap dowel. They were very neatly circular, very tidily flat on both ends, and so closely resembled something bought from a hardware store that they looked a little ridiculous held so delicately in the polyps, or whatever they were, of such formless organisms.

The rods only functioned as communication for the creatures for as long as they remained fairly dry. The rods became too damp to function after something like fifteen minutes of communication. The rods were sourced from trees growing quite a long way away.

Every morning the creatures crawled purposefully, finding their way to the cave mouth and out. They were always gone for two or three hours, and always returned with bouquets of snapped twigs. After making their slow journey to collect the raw materials, the creatures spent the rest of the day carving rods. They accomplished this by finding a sharp bit of rock and rubbing the wood against it, whittling it to extraordinary precision. Perfect little cylinders.

Once each creature had performed this ritual fifteen, sixteen, or seventeen times—depending on how many rods it could hold—it then found itself able to communicate. This they all did, for fifteen minutes or so, until their rods became damp. Those creatures able to hold fewer rods were able to communicate a little earlier, for they spent less time carving; but it is also true that their communication occurred at a significantly lower resolution. And their rods became damp at the same rate, so it is not the case that they were able, despite their lower bandwidth, to communicate for any longer. They simply fell silent sooner.

When its communication rods became damp, a creature would fall completely motionless, and it would remain so until morning, when it would slither off on another long mission to look for fallen twigs. Any given creature seemed never to end up, come evening, next to the creature it had been communicating with yesterday. I hoped, depending on my mood, that these creatures had either a very good memory, or almost no memory at all.

After a very, very long time spent in the company of these creatures, I learned eventually to understand their relentless tapping. How else could I describe what I have just described. For the first several months I was inconsolable. Toward autumn I began, for fifteen to twenty minutes every evening, to get a sense of what their communications were. For the rest of each day I looked for food, I drank water, I masturbated, I slept, I remembered, although less and less, and sometimes I cried. At no point in the first three years did it seem anything other than unbearable and interminable.

It was much later, as I lay on my back on the damp cave floor, and felt the vibrations of these creatures' tapping, that I finally realised they were not communicating only with each other. They were as one, they were a complex circuit, a whole thing, and if I could find the exact position to lie in, then I would encounter the entirety of their tapping as it was surely intended: a message for me.

As I slowly came to understand their pulsing, the complex and intricate torrent of tapping-rhythms began to present itself to me as if it were an image, or even as if it were a moving image. This gale of tiny fragments of auditory information was assembling at last as ideas and emotions. Somehow, I was being communicated with: these creatures knew how I could begin my journey home.

The tapping had me imagining routes and scenarios in my head. I saw images of the way home, but flickeringly, and faint. Once, I saw rope tied on a gate, and I saw how to un-knot it.

At length I realised I was being mocked, or tortured: they knew how I could escape, but they were never going to tell me, not in full. The tapping, since I realised they were mocking me, has felt more than anything like laughter. I had forgotten about laughter.

34 Breakfast of eggs

Breakfast of eggs! Lunch of burger, blue cheese sauce somewhere in there. Dinner of parcelled whiting and bright vegetables, lapped at by golden butter. Breakfast of sliced banana and five prunes, nestled on top of porridge prepared hurriedly by lecturer. Lunch in plastic packaging claiming to have been lovingly prepared. Dog's dinner. Breakfast eaten on fixed, Formica table accompanied by red plastic tomato. Lunch eaten in strong wind on the steps of St. Martin-in-the-Fields before unhappy return to desk job. Dinner of hay eaten by grand clomping horse. Breakfast of quails' eggs eaten by magnificent king. Lunch not yet revealed from one hundred silver domes in splendid ornate hall of gold and white. Dinner refused by young children of desperate parents. Fraught, lonely breakfast assembled intricately, and according to inscrutable rules, by undergraduate with undiagnosed eating disorder. Difficult lunch eaten while holding onto dangling strap in crowded bus. Dinner of exhilarating relief delivered to the door of unfurnished house, on the night of moving in, eaten off of laps while sat on cardboard boxes: shit red wine (two for eight) from mugs and tumblers, insufficient cutlery which takes forever to find, and a truly happy mood. Hungover but joyful breakfast of blazing yellow kedgeree. Lunch of salad, many and varied olives, wide-sliced chunks of cucumber like the cams of some great green engine. Dinner of disappointing pizza. Breakfast of disappointing grapefruit. Lunch of whitebait in enormous tangly mound, arriving with bewilderingly tiny pot of tartare sauce. Unhappy, silent dinner. Much-needed quiet breakfast eaten by exhausted mother who has the house to herself for once, accompanied by pot of coffee and the chance arrival of something lovely in the post. Lunch eaten on the way to something exciting. Bullshit dinner, hurried before night shift, last mouthful still being chewed while washing plate under tap. Breakfast of champions. Lunch of failures. Dinner of poets. No breakfast: on this occasion, a mistake. Lunch which is frugal and shit. Dinner on pebbly shore of barbecued mackerel straight from the sea, along with less recent catches sharpened overnight by wily escabeche: sunset over the sea, and the gig boats yards away on the beach. Breakfast that you and I make together. Lunch prepared with the theme to *The Beiderbecke Affair* in your head. Dinner ordered a quarter of an hour ago, as a treat, from a restaurant with the same name as an ASMR channel which only ever had a single video posted to it, and which the algorithms showed to you a few days after the cute Colorado lad who made the video mistyped the email address of the bakery at which he worked, and sent you his resignation letter. Breakfast of rubbery bacon in crablike, carapaced bap, picked at on grubby napkin, on black plastic plate, on large sheet of paper, on plastic tray, in empty airport café. Overpriced lunch. Dinner of 'medium' mix shawarma and rice which could have fed two of you, and might be the best food you've ever had in town. Breakfast of worm, eaten by bird. Lunch of bird, eaten by cat. Dinner at your friend's house, followed by visit to a restaurant for desserts or cheeseboard: what a treat. Breakfast that your mum eats. Lunch that your dad eats. Delicious dinner which you improvised but which proves an unrepeatable triumph. Communal breakfast prepared as a surprise by student in a new house-share: 'It's fry-up Sunday!' he declares. Enormous, lavish lunch eaten in seconds by youngish man with bulimia and deposited immediately in a lavatory because of a toothbrush rammed down his throat. Dinner which makes you happy. Breakfast which makes you happy. Lunch which makes you sad. Dinner a great deal more enjoyable to prepare than to eat. Breakfast with people you love. Lunch with large, contented animals nearby. Dinner eaten outside, the evening air not too warm.

35 The skyline

The dreams the dog had last night haven't gone away yet. It's like a tinnitus, or a low-level haunting, or like someone's put something in the air, or some committee has, and he knows they've done it, and so does everyone else, but everyone else is inexplicably just fine about it, are all just as silent about it contentedly as he under some baleful unseen duress is silent discontentedly, despite wanting to yelp warning all over the place, despite what's just over not even the horizon but the nearest or the next-nearest thing, which as I shall come to later is in fact simulated.

The dog wanted me to remind you that you are in a room bounded by twelve edges. Over the distances involved it is effectively a single point, but it can often be comforting to conceive of it as a cube.

Each edge is made of some sort of brassy alloy and fitted to an extremely long cable, stretching off in sets of four into the silence. A cube, or more probably a cuboid, suspended in a boring, unremarkable blackness, and whatever each of those cables is attached to off in some infinite deep may well be pulling quite hard, it seems, since the cables aren't sagging. Anyway, depending on how quickly you realise actually that's why there's twelve of them, the dog says, you should think about switching rooms. There's another one suspended in some massive black gap, it will be on the inside at any rate familiar to you.

Are these rooms connected? There are more rooms than are dreamed of in dog philosophy, but not all are in the same universe. If connected, (1) the rooms he speaks of are connected only along cables, with no planks or other means of walking between them; and (2) these cables are of, at the very least, infinite length, in dog infinities, the first of which is seven times smaller than our smallest. The cables are thus of use only to crows and to cats: as infinite in number as in wariness on the one hand, and in indolence and mischief on the other, which is another story entirely.

It is probably crows and cats who did the drawing of whatever the skyline seems to you to be, and Blu-Tacked it on the pane.

36 Twenty-four

C MAJOR

It is a sunny afternoon, and *you* have just had a cup of coffee and some good news!

C MINOR

swiftly establishes a grainy nostalgia to which you are by no means entitled: soaking, relentless rain on enormous Victorian chain-links, dank smog in London streets obscuring sheds of noisy machinery.

C-SHARP MAJOR

is a cube existing in seven dimensions, on each face a different looping GIF of a young deer trying to walk. As for *D-flat major*: the gods and their castles have burned to the ground, and you can breathe again, watching the setting orange sun shimmer on the river.

C-SHARP MINOR

is the humming of the kind of baleful, gloomy deep-sea fish that could produce light, but doesn't. The *bastard.* In fact, he subtracts it from other fish, and from the happy memories of humans up above.

D MAJOR

Greenery, a relief. Some sun again: you can speed up the world as you walk through the woods. You can time-lapse footage of bracken fronds unfurling, and, in fact, you do.

D MINOR

is some sort of flat surface, generated by a motor. Slightly sinister. There might be glyphs on it, I can't tell, they flicker out when you try to look at them, just as the surface itself does. And it's too loud. Perhaps it's a foghorn that never stops, but luckily you can shut the window on it. I don't like it.

E-FLAT MAJOR

Okay. This fat king with a moustache and a red velvet robe is the most pompous thing, but impossible to dislike. He brings jollity to the kingdom.

E-FLAT MINOR

The reality behind a kingdom. I'm sorry you feel like this. Some malformed sob that won't emerge as tears until all your work is done, somehow, and by then you may be too tired for it. It can roll over to another day, an accumulator of already-feeling-beyond-fragile. *D-sharp minor* is similar; you thought ketamine would help, but now you're trapped in a room of polished black wood and can't find the lamp.

E MAJOR

is when you accept you need to take a break, and a long time coming. But this is appropriate enough to its character. It is an honest smile of unexpected relief, like the sudden smell of chopped coriander.

E MINOR

Just the notes E and B, plucked together thousands of years ago, on an instrument with only those two strings, long before the pitches were given names.

F MAJOR

is a kind of startling fact. It's unexpectedly concave, and bewilderingly grid-patterned: like the dent left if you pressed a grand building into the fabric of M.C. Escher's 'Flatworms' and then removed it again. Later, it's 'Sing, John Ball', in K's memory.

F MINOR

is the blueprint for an eternal funeral, a threnody for some infinite and always-lost thing, held in an unimaginably massive building. It echoes with one very loud, very rounded unison F, sounded forever from the brass: they must have learned to circular-breathe. Everything is arranged in fours, in squares. The mourners, the pillars, the trombones. And the organ pipes, some of which are forty feet in diameter. For some reason, out of the pipes come ampersands.

F-SHARP MAJOR

We are in France, and there are fields upon fields of white wooden beehives. Everything's so bright. *G-flat major*: this is it, this is the building you press into the tiled universe to leave the footprint of F-major.

F-SHARP MINOR

A hanging at dawn attended by mist and ghosts. Everywhere ivy, and the condemned man is innocent.

G MAJOR

is another nice afternoon, but you're not really into it. Maybe you're a teenager on a family day out. A drive you don't really want to go on. Fields, hedges, slide past.

G MINOR

Intense communal solemnity. Everyone's heads are lowered in that rare kind of mourning which is deeply felt by everyone. This was not just one single death.

A-FLAT MAJOR

The flat keys tend to be brassy, and this one is a very stable kind of brassy, a structure or scaffold whose many beams are visible, and holding. Buses go in.

G-SHARP MINOR

scurries past in a sort of malign gallop, perhaps a fox hunt. There's revelry, too, and dancing in cosy barns with fires outside. But go careful: the only man who'll agree to play the fiddle when the tune's in G-sharp minor is the Devil.

A MAJOR

Waltzes, mazurkas. It's light outside, and brisk, but not a very bright day: this isn't E major. For whatever reason, the smell of manure as a sign that all is well.

A MINOR

spirits you in a flicker to inexplicable jungles of ice in a pitch-black corridor it will take forever to get through. Occasionally wolf-heads, also made of ice, jut from the wall unseen.

B-FLAT MAJOR

It may be a C trumpet, but that's a B-flat melody: I can't help but think of the solo at the beginning of Ravel's orchestration of *Pictures at an Exhibition*. This is a grand old key, but not an obnoxious one.

B-FLAT MINOR

How is this so Christmassy, while being so dark? It's full of snow (on the ground, not falling), and full of solemn but cosy festivity at night, in parts of the world I have never been to. And, somewhere, whether you can hear them or not, there are Russian basses, hitting ultra-low B-flats in mass.

will beat you at snakes and ladders. It's an expert climber: it's all squirrels and scurrying things, it grows and flowers over trellises, it's footage of ants.

B MINOR

The unshatterable chandelier. Cosmologists describe four similar diamonds grown through each other like a million clasped fingers, locked together forever in space like a tangle of incomprehensible samphires, each one the size of our solar system. The light around them is bent around, and back through them, and always scattered in all directions, however broken, or broken up. We do not know whether they are one thing, or four things.

37 The image, again

Here I am in what we all know is a cliff-side observatory despite the total dark of night, having gone only a few stops on the DLR. I have waited under the yellowy strip-lights for ages in a lengthy snake of a queue, as if at a theme park. What we've all been tasked with involves looking not out of the tempting, long rectangular window—if we could only get closer and push our faces up and block out the light of the room, some formidable, staggering view would be waiting there—but we must face the other way, opposite the glass. Facing that way, back toward the cliff, there are rows of machines we must sit down with. The controls are unfamiliar but easily workable.

The main lever, to the right, controls the image, which is displayed on an apparently functionless screen, at head height, fitted with a black rubber collar which upon leaning forward envelops your head. The lack of glare from the light of the room means the image is more visible. Each time I pull the lever, with my right hand, the image whirs and resets itself.

It's an image of a twilit field, very dark, not very moonlit, viewed from low down, mud everywhere, yellowing grass and other unidentifiable rotting matter; about five inches deep in slushy dark liquid—this liquid is audible, despite the viewer being fitted with no headphones, and my ears still apparently outside that rubber collar. The field is vivid with watery, enzymatic decay. It is full too of hundreds of cows, silhouetted against the heavy blue of the sky, who haven't moved for weeks, just stood there; and they are beginning, through foot rot, or fetlock rot, or leg rot, whatever it is called when some ripe-scented liquefactive necrosis extends further and further up, to melt away into the mud, not so much sinking, just being slowly eroded and digested from the hooves upward.

Every time I pull the lever, the image of the field whirrs away, and in whirrs another, apparently identical. The liquid, the cows, the sky, it all looks the same, it all sounds the same. I pull the lever ten, fifteen times, and everything remains the same. Slowly I realise it is not an image of the same field. Every new image opens up a new version, another reality, an identical field of melting cows in a new universe. They don't seem distressed. You'd have thought there would be more flies. If I were to sit at the viewer, staying with the same field, I might just see them sink into it, very, very slowly; and perhaps the moon might rise, or the sun might even come up.

If you stand and leave the viewer, your image closes. On your return to the viewer a new reality is opened up, also consisting solely of this low-down view of this same field. So that leaving and returning is equivalent to pulling the lever. Having pulled the lever twenty times already myself, and there being hundreds of fellow travellers sat at these banks of machines all figuring out the controls for themselves, I've no idea how many instances of this field must exist. How many must be created, every minute of every day.

Between two panels on the controls is a piece of tatty black plastic which probably they came packaged in, and which must have got stuck there during installation. It is tempting to tear it off, so I do, but it's still there. It never seems to miraculously regrow. It's simply that it's still there. I pick at it, and stare at cows in the dark. I hear the gentle lapping of the water in which they're stood, or into which they're melting, and I still can't figure out how it's audible.

38 York Way

If you leave Euston Station via that side exit, there's a building which has written above its porch the letters 'onevershotst', with the initial 'on' and terminal 'st' in green, so that you can't without further research tell whether it's a restaurant or other establishment called for some reason 'On Evershot St', or whether it's a piece of clumsy design intended somehow to convey the address 'One Evershot St', and which just might achieve this were it in a single colour, allowing the letter 'e' (this is of course all lower-case) to perform simultaneously its two duties—in fact in that case you may read it swiftly as the address, without noticing there is a missing 'e' at all—except that the choice of green for the 'o' and 'n' puts you under such heavy duress to read the 'e' as the first letter of 'evershot', if you don't briefly misread it as 'overshot', that the word 'on' in green is sticking out from the front of it as if a green 'one' has been jammed under it and forced partially out by something applying a greater pressure.

Having just left Euston Station via that side exit, the above was flickering through my head when I felt something strange under my shoe. Had I looked down in time there would have been a discarded nos canister underneath my heel, jammed under it, but it was forced out so quickly from under something applying a greater pressure, me, and set flying, that I saw nothing, instead hearing to my left a ping as it bounced off the upright of a metal handrail. This is all before I saw the pigeon.

Fifteen intensely familiar people immediately walked past me, and in each case, before my face had even a tentative frown of recognition creep round its edges, each obligingly delivered to me that precise section of their CV which contained those films or TV programmes or theatre productions I'd seen them in before. I was grateful for this, as there were fifteen of them, and it would have taken me a while to remember without help.

There was, it turned out, an underground walkway in the newly reorganized King's Cross Station, the only such walkway to be haunted by the ghost of a previous walkway, which had run almost exactly perpendicular to it, such that every now and again an unlucky commuter or tourist about seventeen yards into the shiny-tiled circular tunnel would smack into a ghostly wall, having only faintly seen it before them, and having assumed simply that the approaching slab of ghostly tiling was just tiredness or reflections or shadows. Only character actors survived: other people, civilians, were torn straight down into hell. This was something not one of the actors was able to explain.

Neither was the pigeon, who I will get to presently. There was a baleful character to my imaginings, they unsettled me, as if a single sinister drop of rain, one per human, had caused everyone simultaneously to look up and check: Were there yet again rainclouds to be rustlingly prepared for with changes in behaviour, or fabric?—it had, and there were. As if a man in Smiths had told a woman looking for birthday cards that they did sell them, but that they were very expensive, and as if there was a Paperchase upstairs where they were as little as two pounds. He had, and there was. As if beef and onion crisps were really making a comeback. As if a muscular young man four inches taller than me walking past the York Way McDonald's in thick, dark-grey work trousers had noticed me accidentally lingering over the look of him, and over the imagination of further activity involving even more drastic changes in behaviour, or fabric, for a bit too long, and as if I had met his hostile, frowning gaze by imagining him delivering that phrase I haven't heard since I was a teenager, namely, What are you looking at, you faggot?, and as if I had without a flinch or doubt, shoulders back and my entire body enjoying that sudden readiness for a pounding which makes you feel so glowing and well on a grey day replied, You! You look hot, and hung, and you look up for it. He had, and I had, and he was, and he was.

For obvious reasons I thought I had better walk back to the corner of Evershot St, to check some of the details of this account with the pigeon. The nos canister I mentioned, so the pigeon confirmed, had indeed flown from under my shoe, and pinged off the railing. It had then smacked straight into his face. The pigeon noticed my hesitating, wondering whether he had been correct to use the word 'face', but he ignored me. He then told me a number of things I had failed to notice about our earlier 'encounter'. Far from being bothered by this tiny metal missile, he had simply said to me, 'Welcome to London!', and had continued: 'You ought to know that you just misread "Eversholt" as "Evershot", and were concentrating on entirely the wrong sliding-under of things; furthermore, you are going to find your grey, tedious reality jammed under something else, and forced out, and set flying, by things beyond your wildest imagining which will be revealed eventually to have been applying a far greater pressure. Try to enjoy it without anxiety, as it will not last very long; and I must tell you, Brother Pedestrian, that if you are willing to bring to your afternoon a certain adventurousness of spirit, a young man of exactly the type you are most into is right now crossing Pentonville Road.'

39 A gibet

For the moment, having earlier today woken too late from too much sleep, after a long period of too little, I wouldn't say that I feel insane. More that I feel I am subject to or operating within a different sanity, a distinct and parallel but usually inaccessible kind of sanity. I feel similarly about the sky, which is what I am here to tell you about: that the sky I am visualizing, finding myself unable not to visualize, with all its dry heat and insect noises, all the gorgeous bleakness with which it's so loosely freighted, is impacting more on my mood than the sky I could actually see if I left this café and looked upward, which I did just a few minutes ago, before I came in. Slate grey. It's both a rich blackish blue—this imaginary sky, I mean—and also red: a red that makes me think somehow of lifeless blood, the bleeding of a specifically dead thing, just seeping under gravity, no longer moved by a beating heart. It's cloudless, this sky. The blue that's almost black is the sky of some Looney Tunes cartoon; not just a story set in the Wild West, but a *horror* story set in the Wild West. Shifting transparencies create the impression of tracking shots, and in close-up, coyote skeletons and deathly-dry plant life all slide past in simulated parallax, as in a platform game. But there is no middle or far distance, because the sky is so infinitely deep it flattens off into a background whose colour has some other dimension, the 'key' colour swapped for an absolute and comprehensive darkness, the kind of deep-space you can't ever truly see because there are stars in the way. Flatness which somehow goes on forever. As to its red—this imaginary sky, I mean—I know the one I'm thinking of: Maurice Ravel conjures it for me in his piece 'Le Gibet', part two of *Gaspard de le Nuit*, where it is the backdrop to the hanged man of Aloysius Bertrand's prose-poem. I tried playing it before I came out on this walk. The bell which can be heard from a nearby town is represented by a repeating B-flat, more often than not doubled at the octave. A friend specifically mentioned that repeated bell-note, once, after I had played this piece, saying it had fucked her up. Another friend described the descending chords in the centre of the piece as 'like jazz, with all the joy sucked from it', which is probably why the sky I'm imagining feels so tinctured by blood with all the life sucked from it. I want to play this piece, right now, at a slower speed than I'd have imagined was plausible: about quaver-equals-54. This isn't an impulse toward the kind of 'infinite' or 'ecstatic' slowness with which you're tasked in Messiaen, it's definitely a human slowness; and it shivers through me all the more that the bell sound is so far from anything reassuring—no, here, forever, it partitions into short pulses of time the image of a man hanging from a gibet, against an infinitely deep, blood red sky; he sways almost imperceptibly, in a breeze that barely exists, dry heat and insect noises sliding past as if in a tracking shot, and a gorgeous bleakness settling over everything as the sun slots down below, or behind, the horizon.

40 An ice cube

There are factors come into play after you press the button or notice somebody else has pressed the button which force you into deciding on the one hand whether to be extravagantly in the world and watch the traffic and cross the road as if darting between things or on the other simply to wait until the unlit black square or circle shows a man illuminated in green and you can walk to the other side without even looking, perhaps admittedly with a background sense of peril that the software sustaining the integration of the pedestrian lights and the traffic lights just this once may have failed and that walking toward a green man you may yet be run down: one factor might be the brief memory, your own or not, false or not, of a thirteen year old boy sat in his pants on his bed, in the middle of what he correctly but without much corroboration so far suspects to be nowhere, listening through the insufficiently padded ends of headphones built on such a brittle and thin strip of shiny metal it may as well be a garrotte to music which yearns somehow on his precise behalf for the streetlamps of some city yet to be his, and the gaps between the light they offer; a second factor might be the brief memory, your own or not, imagined or not, of descending staircase after staircase on a ferry to the innermost part of it accessible to the public, somewhere deep in the hull, or at least it feels that way, and of finding a swimming pool there, and of feeling that you can't quite put your finger on what exactly is so wrong and so unsettling about being in the deepest part of a boat on the fucking sea and finding a fucking swimming pool there, no natural light and no noise from the without, and of then feeling violently sick, not from seasickness but from circumstance and the extrapolations of imagination, the image of yourself floating in that comfortably-warm swimming pool, in the deepest part of a boat, on the sea, and holding in your hands just floating it on the surface a bowl of ice-cold water, in which is floating a cup of boiling-hot water, in which is floating a shot-glass containing some very clear and very alcoholic liquid, in which is floating an ice cube; a third factor might be the brief memory, your own or not, false or not, of a quarter-second splinter of memory, the kind which feels like it has exploded, for a quarter of a second, to haunt you all day or all month, into your life, as you decide how to cross a road, from a dream you cannot be sure you ever had, the kind of brief memory which had it been filmed with real equipment would have required the camera to have been on some sort of spiral gantry, such that in the space of a quarter-second it reels back and out and round from being ground-level, in the mud and the muck and recording only the sight of a single struggling-forward-and-through body with all its angularity and elbows and heaviness, to being just about a metre above its initial height, just elevated enough to see that this one struggling-forward-and-through body in the mud and muck is not just one but one of hundreds of thousands, in the same mud and muck, and just elevated enough to see that the space these hundreds of thousands of bodies in mud and muck are in is not open but is somehow bounded, definitely and menacingly, but not in any way quite clear in any experience of the memory, nor in any deliberate attempt to clarify it by replaying it to yourself, and that the hundreds of thousands of bodies apparently just struggling-forward-and-through individually are really and unknowingly part of a colossal algorithm or automaton, the soundtrack, which I haven't yet mentioned, consisting at the beginning of the camera or seeing-vantage's lurch upward back and round of the tail-end of a downward high-string-plus-woodwind yelp, leaving in its disappearance the wrenching slap-pizzicato of an entire cello section, and the sluggish unison of an entire double-bass section on a note which is too low for you to hum, but which you know, even though the quarter-second memory isn't enough to hear what happens next, a note which you know for sure is going very soon to change to a different note, a note lower still, only the memory is cut off too soon, sometimes after even less than a quarter of a second, and obviously you have not yet crossed the road.

41 Stand still

'Standstill' is a fine word, isn't it. The artefact of its own imperative, somehow a point at the centre of what might have been an infinite spiral: a bulletin from here at the dead centre where there is no more movement. Nothing.

To stop, to grind to a halt, is fascinating, beguiling even. It must be something that happens to everyone, but I have wondered whether people who suffer what is called depression have a more intimate or even comradely relationship with standstill. Whether we experience versions of it more often and more complicatedly, know inertia more deeply, or perhaps, whatever this may mean, from the inside, or the other side. Standstill from the dead centre out.

Sometimes a gradually attenuating oscillation may be fixed at one end as the other point draws closer until the gap is zero; just as perhaps the walk—not a circular walk; A, to B, then back to A—which you take along the canal each day goes a little less far, and a little less far the next day, and a little less far again, until one day you realize you are not going for a walk by the canal at all. The length of the journey is presumably in an inverse relationship with your susceptibility to the imperative behind 'standstill'. Sometimes that susceptibility changes, and sometimes abruptly, as when it arrives at an extreme without warning.

Sometimes the oscillation may reduce as if from both ends, as in the attempt, perhaps hungover, to do a partial food-shop without having first made a list. The limited and wayward ambitions of your circuit become attenuated until you are simply if not yet forlornly pacing with a brain made of glass up and down a single aisle, for a short time, simply if not yet desolately, until eventually the easy tos and fros so inertly mimicking a long-factitious purposefulness are revealed slowly to be a simulation, exhausted even of itself, and you find yourself at last motionless, occupying simply if not yet in desperation and nor either under any particular duress some intermediate point between to and fro where you would had you the energy fall on your knees and pray to god, but you do not.

Sometimes a standstill is effected by an outlay of perpendicular energy. Arriving on foot to an apparently silent Queen's Park Road, convinced you will be able to cross it unimpeded, there is suddenly a stream of traffic which continues, and continues, and continues, long enough to have you wonder, from your standstill: *Is this forever?* Or walking east down North Street you are suddenly halted by a queue of people walking out from that thin alleyway, leaving the Lanes, a queue of people which continues long enough to have you asking, from your standstill, the question: *Is this forever?*

Sometimes in a very busy café you will become first in the line only to find that you have to wait a few minutes before a member of staff returns to the till and speaks to you. Meantime, you will see them, from your standstill, all bustling at breakneck speed, so much energy, preparing food and moving order slips from spike to spike. I've worked in cafés and bars and pubs at such times and I think it's important, if you experience standstill at the front of the queue, to accept that standstill graciously. Anyone who doesn't is a Tory.

Imagine you are a mouse, waiting to cross the tracks at Hackney Wick railway station one night, when all of a sudden you are brought to a standstill by something which goes on more than long enough to beg the question: *Is this forever?* A single freight train continues past you, maintains your standstill for twenty minutes. How's it doing that? What is it?

Sometimes I get to the side of a road intending to cross it but do not. I cannot. There is no traffic, but I have nonetheless stopped. Stood still. I am not thinking about anything. Or sometimes in the street I just have no power to keep walking, for some reason, and I find that I am, for a while, at a standstill. Perhaps this is one of these sudden outlays of somehow perpendicular energy.

The perpendicular energy need not be immediately proximate. It's probably something which evens out across the universe. Perhaps creatures on the other side of the solar system are trying to get something done, as if in a busy café; or perhaps an octopus somewhere urgently needs to go in a certain direction, but there's an apparently endless shoal of fish blocking its path—and so it may fall to you, instead, to take on that standstill.

It will then be gifted to the octopus to pass through the shoal unimpeded, just as you may yourself have every now and again found a magical parcel of spare energy, exactly at a time of most need. Next time you are stuck, perhaps somewhere, a butterfly travelling perpendicular to a stampede of rhinos emerged intact.

Look. I don't think this is helping. At the dead centre of standstill you feel dead. To continue to move about is not the behaviour of something dead. Somehow you are moving about again, but your heart feels and hears nothing, remains somehow beating at the dead centre of standstill. Time enough for your soul to beg, of its own irrefragable stasis, *Is this forever?*, while your body yet drags you around.

42 The helpline

Stepping off the 49 one stop too late just as it accelerates again you are briefly in the air and moving sideways relative to everything, a perpendicular version of which motion happens when you finally reach the top of the bus stop escalator, keeping your bare feet right in the centre as its side-brushes have been replaced with three blades, as with a safety razor, and step off from the top into the multi-storey, only to encounter a three foot drop, and as instantly as you discern the sound of shoed hooves trampling dustbin lids, and the stately humming of a bus driver swatting at a moth, you feel suddenly alone except for the portentous presence of hinged brass frames nearby, your body stiffens before landing, and your face smacks the rink, two seconds of silence before you feel it get cold. Both movements are uncannily like being jolted suddenly from sleep, but in neither case can you wake any further up, and the helpline number has gone dead.

43 A loss

On the third day of August, 2021, I tested positive for COVID-19. I had just received my second vaccine. For one week, symptoms were mild. Then the trouble started.

EIGHT DAYS

Now comes the complete loss of smell, and of taste. Nothing tastes, or smells, of anything at all. It hits very suddenly one afternoon, while I am eating, as if a reef of sensors razed in an instant.

TEN DAYS

Strong chemical smell: perhaps ammonia, or ammonia mixed with yoghurt, burning onto a ceramic hob. Not connected with any real-world input, just a constant smell. Taste, or smell: somewhere in between. Already by this time I am forgetting to eat.

APPROXIMATELY THREE WEEKS

Burning chemical smell at last fading. Occasionally the odour of a can of Bouillon which I once found in my nan's cupboard, hunting for jam, with a 'best before' date three years before I was born.

FOUR WEEKS

Certain jars of herbs or spices if inhaled at length smell as they ought to, very faintly. The burnt chemical smell has become more metallic, like fingers which have been fondling a set of keys, or the palms of hands immediately after sliding painfully down steel guy-ropes from wooden telegraph poles. They don't look like they should have so much friction, do they.

FIVE WEEKS

I discover one morning that Braeburn apples taste heavenly, just as they should, and as intensely as they should too. The juices which drip, likewise. Genuine joy for a while until I discover the same is not (yet?) true, sadly, of other things. Coffee for instance smells, if anything, of envelope gum, and tastes like the paint round the end of a yellow-and-black striped Staedtler.

SIX WEEKS

Senses have returned essentially to normal, everything just less intense. As if my nose has the soft pedal down. The one remaining problem is greasy food, which smells (if not tastes) like licking around inside the packaging of a Wall's Solero long past its best, one that's melted and hardened several times. Sometimes the vivid smell of a charity-shop sewing machine.

FOUR MONTHS

Suddenly, a small number of specific and unrelated things, unfortunately including myself, all powerfully smell of rotting red onion. This is distressing and multiple showers a day make no difference. The burnt chemical smell appears at random every few hours, faintly; it now seems mixed with flavours: anchovies, or sometimes over-roasted chestnuts.

SIX MONTHS

A reckless return to greasy food backfires as a Co-op 'Meat Feast' pizza tastes like the smell of the contents of a half-full bottle of Lucozade Original which a Grindr hookup pissed into in 2013 and hid behind a box in my room for me to find three months later. I say 2013 to remind you that Brighton was flooded with mephedrone at the time, and so, as a consequence, were we: just for that extra tang to the bottle, when finally I opened it.

SEVEN MONTHS, TWO WEEKS

No further experiments, not after such a catastrophe; just a gentle improvement and some curious new changes. Smells which are necessary for happiness—freshly ground coffee, chopped parsley (mint, basil, coriander, if parsley is not available), tomato plants—are still, alas, very weak. However: the brief aroma, on entering any room, of Harrison Ford circa *Raiders*. 9/10. I absolutely don't mind it.

NINE MONTHS

Too late, it occurs to me that it could just be that I have forgotten, or lost the knack, of how to make a decent curry. It's been an unprecedentedly weird year, and skills can be lost as much as they can be gained. Ingredients now tend to smell perfectly normal, albeit weak; and it's not that my meals taste *bad*—merely boring. Decision: probably both. Of course you get worse at cooking when your smell and taste is fucked.

THREE HUNDRED AND SIXTY-NINE DAYS

All food tastes like our dearly-departed Brannigan's 'Beef and Mustard flavour' crisps. Sadly, this haven only lasted a few hours. Perhaps the number 369 is significant. I would appreciate hearing from anyone else who experiences this effect, in case it can be found to be replicable.

ONE YEAR

I am sad to tell you that Tunnock's Teacakes, which taste normal, smell of Ilfracombe seafront, and sometimes of Roy Orbison. Tap water smells tantalizingly like coffee, but tastes like flat Carling swigged on a replacement bus service. I'm surprised at how furious this makes me.

ONE YEAR, TWO WEEKS

I do remember being warned that recovery from parosmia is not linear. Still, it is upsetting that things have suddenly got worse again, so far in. Everything is just hot new tarmac and chewed cardamom pods. Even when trying to sleep. I realize it's been months since I tried fresh coriander, and warily bite a leaf off. It tastes foul, truly rancid: I cannot even swallow it, nearly vomit right there in the shop, and I need to run home and rinse my mouth. The only unaffected taste is blood.

ONE YEAR, TWO MONTHS

After six weeks on board, the entire crew are dead, I smell worse than the dog, and the weather when we arrive in Whitby is atrocious. The salt air tastes of keen electricity and I feel fortified in my instincts, unstoppable in my desires.

ONE YEAR, FOUR MONTHS

Deep rich red blood loses most, but not all, of its appeal. This perhaps a case of too little too late, but still a good thing. Now, cruising one night, back in Brighton, I discover by chance a pleasant smell, at last: the vivid hum of the public lavatories in the Pavilion Gardens. They are locked until early morning, but I habitually stand there all night with my nose jammed into the crack in the door. If this can smell nice, then maybe other things can too. It is good to feel hope. In the morning, the police arrive in a stench of bad mussels; and the arresting officer when I lick his face tastes of Copydex, piss, and Ceefax.

Here we are. 'Here' is Waterloo East, where between the arrival boards and the branch of Upper Crust are frequently to be found wafting about three stereotyped smells of home: freshly baked bread (which makes sense), freshly mown grass (which doesn't) and—at last!—I can smell coffee. I have no explanation for this, mind, as the coffee place is always shut. Nevertheless I pitched my tent this morning and have resisted all attempts to move me on. The smell of coffee is as strong in the tent as petrol on a forecourt, but it is gorgeous, and rich, and deep: as dark and as golden as molasses, like velvet made audible, like the cosiest memories made visible and tangible. However, in a dismal and spiteful twist, what coffee now tastes of—and I had to fucking walk to Waterloo proper to find this out—is herbal tea. Report ends.

44 A tab

Stood smoking outside the pub I wound up talking to someone who I found it difficult to listen to, because he picked his lip. I do that too, it's an anxious thing; and I wouldn't usually mention it, except that he drew some species of short-straw I'd never even imagined, and beginning with a tiny tag of spare, dry, proud skin at the top of his lower lip, on his left side, he peeled off downward a strip about a millimetre wide and a centimetre tall (or however tall a lower lip is). I've never known whether there is a name for the edge below which a lip is no longer a lip, and the millimetre-wide strip is continuing to peel down, or off, or both, into an area which in a centimetre or so will be unambiguously designated 'chin'. He had obviously shaved this morning but there were tentative bristles, such that when this millimetre-wide strip of skin was being torn off, there was a visible ping every time it was released from the brief pivot of a spike of stubble, though mercifully it didn't at any point have to be negotiated a little, so as to free it of lengthy beard-hairs (or free beard-hairs of it). When the strip of skin had been peeled long enough that its point of connection with his face was what was definitely the bottom of his chin, he briefly let go of it, I think by accident, let it dangle, looking me very briefly but very anxiously in the face while he did so: it was about two-and-a-half to three inches long now, obviously slightly red from the early leechings of blood, and slightly translucent, and eerily consistent in being about a millimetre wide. It looked like the stripe of plastic with which packets of biscuits or crackers are opened. I believed, I think, that the brief, anxious look was somehow to signify that he had committed to this without really wanting to, as if his hand in this decision had been forced, that he was at the mercy of something: yet nothing about the look he gave made me think he was beseeching me, or indeed anyone, for an instruction to stop what he was doing. So I thought: maybe what's best is if I just let him get on with it. As these thoughts went through my head they distracted me, and when after a second or so I was aware of him again, I saw that he was holding his hand behind his head, at about the height of his ear, and that the strip of skin he had peeled off—now long enough that it couldn't be held taut except ostentatiously or with some effort—had left a raw, presumably excruciating furrow, extending from the top of his lip, curling down under the left side of his chin, round his neck, and further up the back of his neck almost as far as his hairline. That the width of this ribbon of skin was still, constantly, about a millimetre, made me more tense even than the sight of the searingly painful stripe it left behind. It was as if he had a drawstring, or a tab for easy opening—as if everyone had one, but he had just been the first person unfortunate enough to discover exactly how to find it, without ever wanting to. What he had committed to was something I wasn't quite ready to see. The raw, one-millimetre stripe left behind, from what he'd already torn off—going from his lip, his chin, the area where it travelled over his Adam's apple, then round some further neck, curving toward his shoulder, then back upward until it hit his hair—that was a constant sluice of blood now. Unsettlingly bright, not a deep red. He was drunk enough I think that the pain he was experiencing was intense, and expressibly so, but not immediately upsetting, if that makes sense. It was his pain, it was there, he knew what it was and why it was. And it was part of a project. When the strip hit his hairline it became obvious that—unlike with his beard—as he tore it upward there would be hairs through it, which meant the strip of skin had to be far more carefully negotiated, otherwise a hair firmly rooted in the scalp might be strong enough to tatter or even rupture this emergently precious tendril: it was clear at this point that his slender, painful, uninvited ribbon was nonetheless an important event, and that it absolutely had to remain intact. I am glad that he had fairly short hair, but it is true that this unvolitional ritual, as I now realised it to be, slowed down drastically here, where so carefully he found himself teasing the strip of skin apart from his hair without breaking it. When this strip—still a millimetre wide, over a foot long at this point—emerged from his hairline there was a brief period of relief as he tore it down his forehead. It was visibly, and audibly, incredibly painful, but there was relief for sure, which seemed to involve no longer having to deal with the fact of hair. Briefly his eyebrow ruined that relief, but then there were another few centimetres of uncomplicated tearing, from unfollicled skin. Still it seemed always the same width, about a millimetre. It happened that this strip then ended, at the bottom of his upper left eyelid. There was a moment of some decision, where at last before tearing skin from the inside of his eyelid it seemed that enough was enough and he clipped it off. It was loose now, and he held it warily, more like two feet long than one, as the blood poured down into his eye, and out into his hair, and down over his left shoulder, and suddenly a ribbon of skin which had been forever curved was dangling vertical, a tiny sliver of the outside of his head unwrapped and uncanny. He gave me back the lighter I had lent him, and thanked me—we'd been continuing our awkward conversation through all of this—then moved his right hand toward the left of his lip to begin tearing off another strip of skin: it was evident now that before the morning, however long it took, all of the left of his face—except the area between his mouth and the top of his lower eyelid—would be slowly skinned completely, one-millimetre strip by one-millimetre strip. Of course he immediately realised that his right hand was the wrong hand to peel off a ribbon of skin from the left of his face, so with his left hand he screwed up this first ribbon of skin and, after a very brief hesitation, handed it to me. I ate it immediately, because as usual I'd forgotten to have any food that evening; and I decided that when I was back inside, I would every now and again look out of the window, watching him, throughout whatever he had got himself into. Just to see was he alright.

45 A speed of almost zero

Recently in a dream I used an adverb which doesn't exist. It is rare I dream a word which makes sense, any sense that survives in the waking world, yet in this dream there were three. Somebody was accused of 'pamphletative logic', which is a little incoherent and not very interesting. I accidentally described something as a 'nobody of water'; I have written elsewhere about ghost lakes, but not much, so perhaps this was a gentle nudge by way of a brief haunting.

The adverb was 'apochistically'. It seemed to be one of those words which contains two kind of oppositional meanings: on the one hand, 'very definitely', and on the other 'to an almost imperceptibly small but still significant extent, and therefore remarkable for that'. So that one single drop of extremely lethal poison would in a massive body of water be *apochistically* present, if the surface filled with the corpses of fish, and creatures great and small were dropping dead at the shore.

What I said was that something was going 'apochistically slow'—which confuses me further, in that the word seems in that case to get, via another word, tangled up in its own negatives. If what 'apochistically slow' means is that something is moving, but at a speed of almost zero, then surely you could just as well say that it's moving apochistically fast. A visit again from the ghost of Messiaen, and his 'infinite' slowness.

Now I'm fussing over the spelling instead, because the word makes less sense than I thought. As I first wrote it down, it was double-p. I experimented with double-s, but that made the ghost of *pochissimo* too visible; if the dream didn't disclose it as definitively as that to me, I'm not going to do so for anyone else. I believe it would be dangerous.

46 Gheests

I realised, as soon as I left the queue, that when the woman in front of me, having all of a sudden found herself host to a shivering, had said, 'oh gosh—a ghost just walked over my grave!', that I had misheard this as 'oh gosh—a goose just walked over my grave'; and then, having figured out my mishearing, I realised that I felt sure her original utterance was in any case a confusion of two things, the first being ghosts, and the other being the phrase in which 'someone', not specified to be ghostly, 'just walked over my grave'; and I realised soon after *this* that either I must soon myself mishear 'goose' for 'ghost', probably in a figurative circumstance involving not saying 'boo', to which anyway a ghost might always now that I think about it have seemed more appropriate than a goose, or that, as was probably more likely, someone at that exact instant as I misheard 'ghost' for 'goose' must elsewhere have been mishearing 'goose' for 'ghost', probably in a figurative circumstance involving not saying 'boo', to which anyway a ghost might always now that I think about it have seemed more appropriate than a goose, because if neither of those counter-mishearings were to happen, then the notoriously stable equilibrium sustained by ghosts and geese would either be scattered to the four winds or thrown to the wolves (both of which entities, to refer both to four things as one thing and to many things as one thing, are beyond the scope of this essay): unfortunately, this simple negotiation proved attractive for only about twenty seconds, and it occurred to me that the ghosts and the geese brought into being, or unbeing, by the mishearing of the one for the other or the other for the one are themselves a species of ghost, the brief but significant conjurations which result from a ghost or a goose misheard for the other, which means that the equilibrium being disturbed here is not between geese and ghosts but between ghost-geese and ghost-ghosts, which means that even when this more local complication has been solved or counter-balanced, there must also be required a further counter-balancing in order to sustain the notoriously stable equilibrium between ghost-geese and ghost-ghosts and goose-geese and goose-ghosts—an equilibrium whose disruption, if the aforementioned seemed drastic, is quite simply of devastating consequence not only to ghosts and geese, and to ghost-geese and ghost-ghosts and goose-geese and goose-ghosts, but also to you and I and to everyone we know. Be vigilant, will you.

47 A black cat

Another true thing: once, right, I was writing the word 'path' when a black cat with what must have been ill intent went to cross the 't', before I managed to; but it missed, and it crossed the 'h', leaving me with palħ, which is just the word 'pal' and then ħ, which is equal to Planck's constant, h, divided by 2π; and in this case it was presumably then to be multiplied by p and a and l, and since these are unknown quantities I couldn't decide whether it was after all lucky or not; and the only thing I could think of was to try to make the black cat cross the 't's in its own path, which I assumed must be (to distinguish it from mine) a 'catpath', so I wrote 'calpalh', and waited; but that wasn't a real word, and it must have known I was up to something, because it crossed nothing, and I ended up experimenting by writing 'Calpol', which was the nearest actual word I could think of to 'calpalh': but the black cat, instead of crossing either 'l' to make it into a 't', just wrote the letter 'h' on the end; and before I knew what I had done, I had somehow crossed that instead, ending up with 'Calpolħ', which the black cat crossed out and corrected to 'ħCalpol', only to cross that out and simply replace it with 'h'; so I suppose what the black cat was trying to tell me is that Calpol is equal to 2π, which is information I don't know how to use but certainly won't forget.

I have often wondered what might have happened if the cat had done as I had hoped in my experiments, whether it had crossed letters to produce 'catpath' or 'Catpot', but I think it's probably for the best that it didn't; and besides, while what might have happened I may never know, I've learned something.

48 That summer

That summer, C and I exploded out of school into the sunny glare of the holidays, we must have been about eleven, and we were wiry and quick in our shirts and shorts; we tugged our ties off and threw them into the hedge, and ran back to his house, ran through the kitchen, ran past his brother's dark bedroom, ran out into the garden, our shirts crisp and white in the heat, and playing at guns, the index finger together with the middle and the thumb enough, we ducked and hid and leapt and soon enough climbed over the fence, into the next garden, and then the next, and we trampled, not deliberately but unavoidably, flowerbeds, and vegetable patches, we stole berries and disturbed soil, smacked nasturtiums and hollyhocks to the ground, pretending, not knowing what they were, that they were nettles, and we pocketed strawberries for later, we tore scaled fence by scaled fence to the last garden, with no real idea why we were running, and it was C who landed in this last garden first, shouting his gun noises pchw-pchw-pchw, unseen by me until I dragged and smacked myself up against this last dividing fence, the tiniest fear in my memory now of splinters but nothing like that then, for it was my turn to shoot back, and after three tries, the first of which involved a stumble, to haul myself up, onto the top of the fence, I straightened at last my arms, weight all on the hands now, palms flat and wrists angled like a corner, my waist at last above the top of the fence, my whole upper body there, triumphant, wiry and quick in a crisp white shirt, the left and only breast pocket without my having seen it suddenly stained a horrific red by the squashed fruit within.

There I was, staring down from the top of the fence at C, crouched, his hand a gun, pchw-pchw-pchw, a half-second away from making my own hand into the same shape myself, and making in the most exuberant retaliation the same noises: that is what I was about to do, never minding what either of us might or might not do next, except that then he saw that bright shrill-red patch of stained shirt above my heart—and he screamed, still pointing a gun at it. I started, lost my grip, the top of the fence hit the bottom of my chin, my mouth smacked shut, and the next thing I knew I'd hit the soil and badly bitten my tongue.

49 Showerhead newly installed

Showerhead newly installed! Showerhead that makes you jump by starting very suddenly, after a gap of three and a half seconds. Showerhead that looks like a dragon. Showerhead that looks like a lamprey. Showerhead whose blue rubber looks crusted, as if with barnacles. Showerhead which you discover after a year of use can be adjusted, to deliver water in thinner streams at higher pressure. Showerhead in so lavish a setting it seems wrong that it doesn't appear immediately to have any settings beyond on and off; you wonder what you are missing, and where it is to be found. Showerhead which remains obstinately inactive and you're too shy, or too lazy, or both, to ask the guy you met last night a second time how to operate it. Showerhead which produces a pitch two octaves above middle D and bends it gently upwards when the temperature is decreased and downwards when it is increased, though the relation does not seem to be perfectly controllable. Showerhead which must be removed from its cradle in order, as if gently coaxing it, to start the water going, for some reason, and then replaced: you have been there too, and you empathize with it. Showerhead in your friend's mum's house. Showerhead outside, with sheep audible beyond a metal door that doesn't reach the ceiling, and an indistinct clatter of tent-zips and breakfast on portable gas stoves. Showerhead which recalls a piece of machinery in the supposedly inhabited world of a computer game, in that it requires the starting of two generators and the positioning of three separate switches and levers, all of which are stupidly, infuriatingly distant from each other. Showerhead of bulbous white plastic whose individual shafts of water vividly recall needles, and are ridiculously inefficient somehow at the basic task of making you wet. Showerhead of blockish metal design whose height adjustment mechanism is fucked, in the flat of someone much shorter than you. Showerhead with four settings, one of which feels vaguely like an enjoyably forceful douche, and about which you tell three people. Showerhead in perfect working order except for one drip near the wall, eventually revealed in explosive 'house meeting' to have been irritating all five undergraduates: the absurdity of this revelation so violently expressed swerves the meeting, oddly, to a welcome access of reconciliation. Showerhead in the dark, four feet and two inches above desperately depressed Ph.D. student who has been sat cross-legged and unmoving for forty minutes now. Showerhead that has a bit of marmalade on it, somehow. Showerhead that has a bit of cum on it, somehow. Showerhead that has a pink shower-cap hung on it when not in use. Showerhead in the film *Psycho*. Showerhead that just looks a bit wrong. Showerhead which produces an uncanny feeling of being rained on; and those drops of water that don't land on you sound somehow as if they are landing on rhododendron leaves. Showerhead in a hotel room, glanced at on the way to dry off and tackle the last of your packing, with the accidental acknowledgement that it's the last interaction you'll have with it.

The glitch is that clicking on both showerhead three and showerhead four will take you to the same location. The shower is a small oblong chamber with, in one corner, an upright rod of metal. Perhaps that chamber is what is properly called the 'shower room'. Either way, do not forget that it must be powered before you can use it: you must start two generators and position three separate switches and levers, all of which are some distance from each other.

Around three of the four sides of the shower room are stood various bottles of shampoo and shower gel, slightly clumped to reflect who they belong to, but not very convincingly; they look glum, like hooded monastic figures exiled from an Escher-staircase, disappointed to be dotted along only three edges of a thing, three edges which lie in a plane and are taken together far from impossible.

Attached to the metal rod, and snaking maybe one and a half times around it, is what looks like a similar metal rod, flexible because subject to extreme rifling; more likely, it is upwards of one hundred smaller segmented pieces of metal, not unlike vertebrae, and likewise hollow, since through all of them must run an impermeable tube, carrying in this case water rather than nerves, although sometimes when the whole is at its most dragonlike you could be forgiven for wondering.

At the top of all this is the head, peering down with a kind of contained imperiousness, the sleek metal exo-skull flaring out to a flowerhead of gunk-encrusted plastic circles, as if a lamprey could 'gape'.

This is the part actually called the 'shower', most likely. Set to its highest temperature it breathes water as a dragon breathes fire, and just as hot. It breathes this, as if shy, straight into the nearest corner, most of the fire hitting the opposite wall, some hitting the adjacent, and running down both as hot water. However, it's at its most dragon-like when you coax it to breathe cooler fire.

What this means: clearly, the dragon breathes hot and cold water in a mixture from two different sources, the balance of their mixing controlled by a lever. The cold water, but not the hot, is at such an enormously high pressure that when pumped through the body it unwinds that lizard-like stack of vertebrae from one and a half to just under one full turn of the upright metal rod (these figures are approximate).

To put it another way: as just happened this afternoon, I tugged the dragon's tiny wing to get it to breathe cooler fire, which it did, but at the same time it swung round and breathed it right into my face, where it transformed as it hit my eyes into tepid water and I yelped like a ghost and whirled like a mad thing.

The failed staircases of shampoo did not do so well out of this and it took me a while to replace them, probably incorrectly. It could be that the engine does not remember where you have moved them to, so that they will, when you return, be exactly where they were before.

50 Poetry

Since the 1970s, poems have been declining at alarming rates. Numbers are starting to recover now, but in order to secure their future, we need to find out much more about them.

A poem is a procedure in a criminal justice system. It is the act of apprehending and taking a person into custody (legal protection or control), usually because the person has been suspected of or observed committing a crime.

Organizations such as Andrew Motion, Carol Ann Duffy, or Simon Armitage, are surveying public areas, but some of the key habitats for these little guys are actually to be found in your back garden. Ponds are important for many amphibian poems.

After being taken into custody, a person can be questioned further and/or charged. Sometimes a poem is also done after a court warrant.

We are lucky to have three native species of poem here in the United Kingdom: palmate, smooth, and great crested. You should not attempt to capture them. As a safeguard against the abuse of power, many countries require that a poem must be made for a thoroughly justified reason, such as the *requirement of probable cause* in the United States.

The best way to find poems is to simply look for them in your pond just around sunset using a torch. You can also find them in your garden hidden under slabs of concrete or piles of bricks.

Furthermore, in most democracies, the time that a person can be detained in a poem is relatively short (in most cases 24 hours in the United Kingdom and 24 or 48 hours in the United States and France) before the detained person must be either charged or released.

51 A hade

Very few hades mentioned in documents have ever been found, and recently (in the last five hundred years) there are almost no accounts of their being discovered by accident, stumbled upon. These strange places were long supposed to be a fiction. The one we visited was, as are all hades, located in the woods. It was somewhere in West Sussex, in a stretch of ancient woodland which has long been known as 'Hayde' or 'Haide'.

We arrived early, one autumn morning. Everything had a look of being very slightly translucent, and the light was pinkish. The departing tutor was already there, ready to ease the handover and generally show me the ropes. She had asked everyone to bring clocks, which functioned somehow as a way of getting the students talking, but after a while they just became curious objects, meaninglessly present.

The students found it increasingly difficult to concentrate, and found they were having thoughts about things like laundry, or cooking: domestic, cosy, familiar things. There was an animal skull, fragile and the size of a fist, with papery coverings to the eye-sockets, hanging from a broken, rotten gate, which was half buried in leaves. Accidentally, I damaged this skull, while nervously alerting the students to its presence.

My colleague could not disguise how anxious she was about what I had done. The students too were uneasy.

It was no longer clear to us, we weren't sure, if there was supposed to be an actual aperture here, which we might walk down—or, more likely, just peer down—or whether simply by being in this place we were enough in both worlds to be slipping away into the other already.

Our sense of purpose repeatedly drifted, but eventually I gathered myself, and began to make some remarks about the qualities of the woodland (and the latitude, proceeding thereby to the ecology), drawing comparisons with specific descriptions of haunted or otherwise frightening woods, in literature and film, and having the students discuss whether those books and films more or less knowingly depict such hades as this.

Soon, we focused in on the fact of slime, in its various tropes and guises—the very specific horror of creatures which lick your face. The class struggled to gather their thoughts, but did decide that it's not erotic. We asked, is the presence of saliva in such instances a kind of digestion? Disgusting, and frightening, not just because happening to the face, but also because beginning far too early, far too outside of something's stomach? If it is some sort of social ritual, then perhaps your status as human is called into question by being affectionately, welcomingly groomed in such a way. As this discussion petered out, the students become even more uneasy and confused. One or two sat on the ground and cried.

We were unable to say for sure whether or not we had been discussing real, recent events. Certainly some of us seemed to have great slicks of mucus, or saliva, on our faces and clothes, and in our hair. The skull was draped with it too. My colleague was less and less often to be found. We were there for hours, or perhaps days, without dawn ever breaking. One or two of the students seemed to have gone, but their clocks, dropped with the others in the leaf-mould, were still there. Some clocks were completely encased in mucus.

The earth-light seemed to darken further as we all became visibly less substantial, more made of that other light. My thoughts kept returning to the wafer-thin paper coverings on the eye sockets of that pear-sized skull which I had damaged, as if in doing so I had imperilled us all: but as it slowly got darker, we milled, indifferently, less and less sure of who each other was, all of us in a translucent, slightly pinkish fog. We no longer realised how much we were forgetting. Why was it we were there? We must have had a reason. I began to remove the piles of leaves from around the rotten gate, in case it could be propped up and made to open.

52 Funicular

Half past four the temperature is sixteen thousand degrees the steepest A-road in the country smells of brake-pads and pheasant blood it took nineteen men to carry the coracle through the storm when the lake was drained they found two shoes and a small mirror the weir had been famous locally for hauntings in any case there was the tale of the vicar who boiled parishioners in acid several small piles of stones were left on the beacon which was named after an old word for the area not an actual bat fires were lit bay boleti and stinkhorns were visible in the woodland and from a distance the rotting magpie carcass seemed filled with marbles but for now the smell of brake-pads and pheasant blood is a familiar enough threat the temperature is sixteen thousand degrees about twelve metres of the circle-pocked edging strips to old printer paper are draped over a nearby mountain ash or hawthorn most of the varieties of apple on this hill were saved from extinction by a single schoolteacher they taste of brake-pads and pheasant blood the steepest A-road in the country is hissing into your feet in the sun if you put the coracle down you will stop sweating but don't do that in any case they acknowledge the importance of getting the coracle to the weir without contaminating the lake with brake-fluid and pheasant blood everybody who lives at the bottom says that one day a funicular is coming they call it the installation some kind of interim rope system has been suggested but this in relation to the coming funicular installation is treated as if it is somehow blasphemous.

53 Mrs N.

It was crucial in the instincts of Mrs N. that she should, on entering the kitchen, be the first to say something. That had been her way since early middle-age and it was to remain a fixity. But with people variously engaged it was not always obvious to her what she should say, when suddenly appearing in the kitchen she spoke.

Obviously it could not be in response, or she would not have spoken first, so she preferred initially at least to speak first with the benefit of immediate context. She would look quickly at the dish being prepared or the vegetable being chopped and make some immediate remark which she considered more often correctly than not to be relevant. Though this ratio changed over the years. And later she settled, instead of uttering some immediate remark (which she considered in her earlier years more often correctly than not to be relevant, and in her later more often incorrectly than not) into the habit of delivering one of a set of familiar phrases.

These phrases it would be pleasant to think were those which you, or I, or she, depending, could describe as her favourites, but it is more likely that they had snagged themselves for some other reason in her fraught inventory of habit, seeming as it could come to seem more often than not more like an arsenal. Perhaps the reason was some combination of their speed and their utility, for over the years this set became just the two phrases. By no means did this honing involve an increased precision in the phrases; on the contrary, the attenuation of their number to a mere two was only possible because the phrases themselves contained vagaries. Instead of doing the work of adapting her immediate remark to a given context, Mrs N. had settled after many years into deploying one of two phrases, each of which she had by consideration or long experiment deemed more often correctly than not to be adaptable in almost the extreme.

One of them definitely carried with it a glow of approval, not necessarily of the person it was addressed to, but certainly of whatever it was they were preparing. It was 'Ah, yes, that'll do you'. The other was even more adaptable, ranging as it could depending on her delivery, which she chose more or less deliberately, from comradely fatigue to severe opprobrium: 'Ah, the same old lengths'. It is worth noting that the punctuating 'yes' was an optional extra, which she may have thought of as like salt and pepper, to be applied according to one's taste or whim, and certainly never to excess, but most likely did not.

There was a difficulty. To recap: having so fine-tuned her reserve that it contained only two imm-ediate phrases, one of which was approving, the other of which could range depending on her mood and her delivery from comradely fatigue to severe opprobrium—specifically:

1. Ah, [yes,] that'll do you;

or

2. Ah, [yes,] the same old lengths;

—she still had of course to make some choices. Initially the choice was of which remark to make, and then in the case of it being the more flexible of the two, she had to choose in what tone to deliver it. And to make this choice, or these choices, she had over the years learned to look quickly at the dish being prepared or the vegetable being chopped.

This method slowly lost its efficacy at a rate consistent with Mrs N.'s loss of her sight. This might have been solvable by her gliding over to the dish being prepared or the vegetable being chopped, but in the time taken her in crossing the kitchen, which is never zero in a kitchen which has size, the other person might have spoken first. This axiomatically could not happen. Of course her sight itself was being lost at a rate consistent with the slowing of her movements, so there was a multiplicative aspect to her difficulties.

Quite simply in solution she elongated the initial 'Ah' with which her chosen phrase began, saying it immediately as she entered the kitchen, potentially at quite some volume, so as to be sure to be uttering first. Mrs N. then continued producing this vowel until she was close enough to look quickly at the dish being prepared or the vegetable being chopped. This transit could in her later years take half a minute, with the accompanying noise she produced resembling to most people's ears a Dalek in pain, if anything.

As an aside, it came to be the case, as her journeys became slower, and the 'Ah' longer, a great deal more likely that she should include the punctuating 'yes' upon arrival. It was probably a marker of relief at this late stage.

For the last three years of her life Mrs N. was completely blind, yet on entering a given kitchen she still produced without fail a vowel, in this final period lasting sometimes up to five minutes, with intermittent gaps for breath. Some may say that this latter aspect may render plural a vowel to which I have referred in the singular. It is true in either case that on entering a given kitchen she produced a vowel, and, if the contention is also true, it follows that she produced afterward several similar vowels. She did not always continue with a phrase in her later years, having forgotten probably why she was doing what it was she was doing.

Lastly: nobody was ever sure, completely blind as Mrs N. was, how she could be completely sure she had entered a kitchen. A change in temperature is a possibility, both in general and as an explanation for how Mrs N. could be completely sure she had entered a kitchen.

In all other aspects of her life she was happy, and in the matter of the events on her entering a kitchen she was if nothing else the first to make a noise.

54 London

Sleep paralysis, or a waking nightmare, as dawn broke, with a single poem as guide. My eyes opened but no part of me would move, and unable to make a noise either I looked in the only direction I could look, toward the window, to see what seemed to be a stooped old man who for sure meant me harm, except that he was too old to move; and immediately I had in my head the entirety of 'London' by William Blake.

After the first two lines—I wander thro' each charter'd street / Near where the charter'd Thames does flow—the Thames started dripping through my roof, which was fine, this roof often used to rain, but at the same time I became aware of that adjective *charter'd* which had swung out from the first line and now with its whole weight was smacking back in *charter'd* and reverberating through the rest of the poem; it swung back again and again, back and forth like the action of a Newton's cradle, marking everything *charter'd*, and my memory of the text bristled out and out with it and made it almost impossible to remember because as I went further and further on the word had smacked back in and rewritten it almost to the point of obliteration: this is only an approximation, but by the third pass, clack, clack, clack, it would have looked something like this, but changing all the time, *charter'd* relentlessly smacking through it and furring it up as if with crystals, or mould: I wander thro' each charter'd charter'd charter'd charter'd street, Near where the charter'd charter'd charter'd charter'd Thames does flow And mark in every charter'd charter'd charter'd face I meet charter'd charter'd charter'd marks of charter'd charter'd charter'd weakness, charter'd charter'd charter'd marks of charter'd charter'd charter'd woe. In every charter'd charter'd charter'd cry of every charter'd charter'd charter'd Man, In every charter'd charter'd charter'd Infants charter'd charter'd charter'd cry of charter'd charter'd charter'd fear, In every charter'd charter'd charter'd voice: in every charter'd charter'd charter'd ban, The charter'd charter'd charter'd mind-forg'd manacles I hear How the charter'd charter'd charter'd Chimney-sweepers cry Every charter'd charter'd charter'd blackning Church appalls, And the charter'd charter'd charter'd hapless Soldiers sigh Runs in charter'd charter'd charter'd blood down charter'd charter'd charter'd Palace walls But most thro' charter'd charter'd charter'd midnight streets I hear How the charter'd charter'd charter'd youthful Harlots charter'd charter'd charter'd curse Blasts the charter'd charter'd charter'd new-born Infants charter'd charter'd charter'd tear And blights with charter'd charter'd charter'd plagues the charter'd charter'd charter'd Marriage hearse come the charter'd charter'd charter'd charter'd charter'd charter'd charter'd charter'd charter'd charter'd plagues (the line-breaks all fallen away) and now there was a map of London on the old man's head which was a diagram of veins shot through with poison, straight lines and curved corners; this design was named using a word-choice from *Discipline and Punish* mixed up with something Dickens once wrote (unless the sleep paralysis made that up): *The Capillary Extension of Debt* it was called, and it was here designed by a draftsman called Hurry Back, and tattooed or carved into the poor man's head in bright colours—in fact, the old man *was* Hurry Back—and scraping, scalloping his skull from the outside, that way that syphilis does from the inside (unless the sleep paralysis made that up) and oh my heavens the noises he was making—Hurry Back, stood there creaking and groaning, suppurating from a map of debt and clap carved into his head, and what we shall here call capital smacks through the Newton's cradle of the poem and now only one word in a billion isn't 'charter'd'. Where on earth have all those letter 'e's gone? The room fills with the roaring Thames. This went on for only a few seconds, but it felt like an age. I heaved my mind into waking the rest of me up, the sound of a yawn tore physically through me, and then there was silence. The Thames was no longer dripping through my roof, and Hurry Back was a lampshade and a pile of clothes.

55 Latches

Gaily through wind and weather you walk into an underfunded moon pond of barbed wire and latches and the barman says, Why the long Sigur Rós playlist? An entire vigour field of anguish and Hollandaise horseshoes crosses the road to a potent laxative ostinato, and the trick of all this green-shelled cartilage was always bolder than the rotation of their helper skeletons billowing into some computer program about money that dickheads use, or Ceefax. Imagine exactly that. Peter Falk plays himself not just in the 1987 Wim Wenders film *Der Himmel über Berlin* but also in ordinary human life. Peter Firth is in the films *Letter to Brezhnev* and *Equus*, especially in comparison to other films. Now. I am a drawing of a hangover. A small drawing. A horſe walks into the underfunded moon pond of barbed wire and latches, and the barman says, Why the long s? A small drawing of a resplendent hangover. But what else walked into standard sealant practice is a muscular rendering of vague and truncated risk, such as thirty razor-strop Swarfega canapés propelled through the hefty catalogue like a molasses of fossilizing Shards; and a bad finance joke is to be thrown on top of a shed and pecked at until it bleeds wire-wool from its feathers, nesting in a *Van der Valk* box-set and clogging the corners with shit that smells like a Copydex croissant, or a pain au chocolat rescued from five urinals. You try to leave the underfunded moon pond of barbed wire and latches, but the barman says, Why the long interview, filmed outside a horrible pub in Islington, with the white ball from *The Prisoner*, focussing almost entirely on its career since the 1987 Wim Wenders film *Der Himmel über Berlin*, and ordinary human life? You do not hear this question, and you would have thought it preposterous if you had. In the skate park, dogs tell jokes about Peter Falk and Peter Firth, but their bums melt, excruciatingly. Up through the concrete spurt ejaculatory beanstalks of molasses, Copydex, piss, Ceefax. Someone must be under arrest. You keep caps-lock on until you have played yourself in the 1987 Wim Wenders film *Der Himmel über Berlin*, an underfunded moon pond of barbed wire and latches, Ceefax, The Shard, *Van der Valk*, *The Prisoner*, *Letter to Brezhnev*, *Equus*, and ordinary human life, and until the sound of latches confirms to all who wish to know that the gates of the moon pond are shut.

56 Titivilus

It has been known since the 13th century that during the Christian sacrament of the Eucharist (also 'Holy Communion', or 'Mass') words which are stumbled, mumbled, or otherwise wrong can be seen to escape: just slightly proud of that speech which is sanctioned or correct, they manifest literally, physically (regardless of the species of mass) as a minuscule nugget or speck; the instant these specks are exposed to air they begin to fur up with crystals like the filament of a kettle, a tiny rose of scallops and shards—and under this new weight, as it grows, they fall, about as far as the feet, and there!—in a ribbon of flickered sulphur—perhaps a deep, shrill flame, visible and gone, like a strip-light soared past by a speeding train—there above the ground they are snatched away, by a hellish magpie of glitches.

He is in the employ of Belphegor, and his name is Titivilus: the demon who thought to strategize the hoarding of errors. Those little crystals of wrong speech will count against you, it is said.

When an entire congregation speaks or sings together, the errors may become so numerous that Titivilus cannot catch them all before they hit the ground; you may hear clatterings, may have already mistaken them for dropped or knocked objects, or the crack of a creaking pew. Perhaps this, in combination with the capacity of the clergy to persist through unmanaged alcoholism, is one explanation for the felted floor around the altar. Think how many such ceremonies, and therefore how many tiny mispronunciations or off-kilter emphases are happening simultaneously in a single town, let alone the world over: yet this demon is still electrically fast, such that to look over at a clatter is in every case to be too late to see the error which fell. Even if it shattered as it landed, he'll have got the tiny shards, and all the dust, already.

M

In certain accounts across Europe—in which he is often mistaken for the Devil himself—Titivilus occurs occasionally as a mystery visitor to an inn. These tales may involve his playing an impossibly difficult tune on the fiddle, perhaps one which causes the company to dance until they collapse; or sometimes he is said to have exhibited fiendish displays of magic, extraordinary winnings in card games, and so on—but in every case, that is a confusion in the telling; definitely all this is the business of other demons. Or, indeed, of the Devil.

Titivilus, as I have said, is specifically a wrangler of wrong speech, during solemn ceremonies: so why is he appearing in taverns, of all places? Perhaps we know so little because the accounts are so rare—the effects of his trick are not immediate. In the moment it is barely detectable. The ceremony he forms, although immensely powerful—just as powerful as any mass—mimics a more mundane communal gesture: the toast.

He is not always successful. The trick is most likely to work in cultures which tend in these rituals to maintain eye-contact. Glasses or tankards are clinked together, with some hearty toast or another; yet, in the infinitesimal lull which follows, that moment of susceptibility in which a conjurer might misdirect, in that moment Titivilus inscrutably commands attention, as does an open fire—and just at the brink, where each vessel is almost touching the lips—his own glass to his mouth as well, of course—he intervenes, perhaps a shade quieter, but very distinctly, with the name of his superior:

Belphegor.

Here too a ceremony has been formed: a ritual in which wrong speech may manifest as an airborne speck, and Titivilus perceives a beat, during which he takes the ceremony from safety to something else altogether, splicing a moment in which everyone present—although they may be unfamiliar with the toast—decides, unaware of the danger, to commune nevertheless: to *join in*. That flicker of decision dances about his companions' faces the way sunlight flecks the filaments of a spider-web. An almost-confident, definitely cavalier chorus of unfamiliar, all-too-earthly syllables:

Belphegor!

Never is anyone's mimicry exactly correct: such is his strategy. The 'b' and 'ph' of this demon's name sit uncannily between voiced and unvoiced; the 'g' is not something our vocal equipment can quite complete; the terminal 'r' is not any sound familiarly denoted that way. Perhaps humans cannot correctly produce the true name of this demon at all: this isn't known, probably because it is generally considered extremely dangerous to try.

So. Before each mouth, just proud of the surface of the ceremony, appears in the air a tiny piece of grit, a speck, too small to be seen even as it reacts on contact with the fresh-hexed air they are breathing; and so into each raised glass falls a marker of wrong speech. As imperceptible as it is immediate, the crystal dissolves, and each liquid changes colour—very slightly darker, very slightly more opaque. The company proceeds to drink: their intoxicants of choice cursed in an instant by a verbal error into which, with however small a hesitation, they plunged, oblivious. The effects of this deception are not immediate.

57 A thing forever

Footage of the building being detonated is played forwards then in reverse then forwards then in reverse and in time when you accept it the footage is defibrillated as if each of those devices is a corner of your stupid heart engorged and cavernous they pulse their spiral way down the canopy of fatty tissue and the foul sluicing and the stench of sweet explosive sweats out in wrong colours from your eyeballs and your fingertips and like blueing contused nails ready to drop your skin hardens slate-grey and the footage continues in its pulsing spiral, corners of building falling and coming together, falling and coming together, back and forward and back and forward, crushed into an upsetting pun on 'raised' and 'razed', and steel beams stick from your heart and out of every bifurcation the stench of sweet explosive played in reverse, now get high on concrete dust and smack back down again, you should get a job my friend as a thing forever violently winched to the exhilarating distilled canopy of your own pulsed dereliction, the stench of sweet explosive, I said, you should get a job, mate, as a thing forever violently winched to the exhilarating distilled canopy of your own pulsed dereliction, the stench of sweet explosive.

58 A communication

Any event in a diary or set of diaries or diary-copy or set of diary-copies is recursively an instance of locally administrative probability, and iteratively a juggled gristly clump swirling underfoot in the dust between the lions guarding your assigned fountain, who are batting it in dangerous play. The sinews of it fray until to eat it becomes irresistible, and they never do clean the blood from their lips before returning to the office. No wonder your name is not on the list. Must you feel lost in the system again. Must you. Let me check that for you. The system you are lost in to the repeating sound of a crashed hyena may pass through its own surface until the flowchart spins beyond spreadsheets as we have hitherto understood them and into a kind of spiral-wrapped fistula of absent verve, some species yet to be identified of *We should have contacted you about this: I can only apologise*. This being the case it is recommended that you contact the rhinoceros for more information. He will give you a number for the hippopotamus, who after no more than six (6) days will recommend that you contact the rhinoceros. A giraffe in this context would be kindly, would keep your welfare in mind: it might fetch you a coffee, or even loan you objects. Imagine a giraffe lending you a pen! Return it. The zebra will be accompanied today by three school-age zebras on work experience: Barcode (12), Ray (12), and Twelve (13). Please let us know if they want anything to eat. The hyena may be restarted, but the record of your appointment will be scratched, and rotating at the wrong speed, which as with almost all absent diaries or absent sets of diaries or absent diary-copies or absent sets of diary-copies defaults to zero (please note that zero will appear on the system as -1, because the symbol '0' is reserved for another meaning). Beyond the sandy membrane the sloths of last scattering generate lavish fields of gravity, dark matter, desire, compulsion, and duress, to tip you on your doleful way, in the manner of hunger, infatuation, or space-time. This is a legal requirement, to ensure that the loss of an appointment is always more absolute than the loss of your patience, which is incomplete, stretched in a thread to the end of tomorrow, thinner than a spider's frenulum but persistent and obstinate across the vast marble of the committee room, and more than that, stunningly beautiful. Such power in something so delicate. An elephant couldn't snap it. The rumours that they always try are true.

59 Birds

BARN OWLS

are the artefacts of trying to rotate a papyrus cylinder in the complex plane. Barns were a later invention, named after barn owls as a precaution.

FLAMINGOS

evolved on purpose, and in order to make a slightly passive-aggressive point, from only those calligraphic flourishes discarded with sharp heartbreak on a twenty-ninth of February into a silent lake of ink and rock-salt. You can eat them, but I wouldn't.

GEAR-GULLS

These are adolescent gulls which in their youthful exuberance solve a version of the three-gear problem, perhaps only once in their lives and certainly never in adulthood. They loop in the sky around not a single circle but around a circle or pattern formed of several smaller circles. The problem is trivial for even numbers of circles, but even the Greeks knew that gulls never do an even number of anything. Our solutions to this genre of problems generally resort to higher dimensional space, but the whirling of gear-gulls does in fact lie in a plane: they solve it simply by being adolescent gulls, a technique with which mathematics has not yet caught up.

GEESE

The honk of a goose is extruded from its vocal forge at such high pressure that the grain is moved away from the start of the sound and fills the entire vowel like the crunch of a gearbox, a hurdy-gurdy, or the sudden application of a powerful brake to the wheel of a freight train. Only to us do these noises sound hectoring. As with many birds who so often appear to be just really stressful, they are in fact reassuring each other. This is why the song says 'geese allaying'.

GOLDFINCHES

learn young that there is infinite colour in the world, and never worry again that their blazing wings are depleting or exhausting it at source.

HAILSTONES

You get them in the air and they go fast. I like the ones where you are looking at some grass. The hailstones hit the ground so fast that you can't see them land, so that when they become visible, bouncing just an inch or two above the grass, it looks like they are hatching and immediately trying to jump.

I do wonder what these things mean, if anything. Their 'default' noise is so reassuring, and gentle; it emerges and trills like spring water, different scurryings reflecting light as you watch from different angles. A very light brook over pebbles. Yet also it has a soft grain to it, rarely more than the flesh of a pear. Perhaps when they're very alarmed, a rattle of ball bearings.

It sounds sometimes like the production of that noise is so close to merely breathing that the distinction is more of a smudge, a grey area, as if to chickens the concepts of *voiced* and *unvoiced* deform with continuous flow into each other as may vowels in one of our diphthongs. We cannot know for sure that chickens haven't thought about this, and haven't just as much of a vocabulary for linguistics and phonetics as we do. We cannot and we must not.

Maybe sometimes that's why they make me want to clear my throat: not knowing whether that sound was deliberate, or not. Sometimes I think it isn't deliberate, but that they also don't try to stop it, because it contributes to a cosy, ambient consolation. The rippling sound of each other remaining alive, a soft rill only just proud of breath.

Smudged as the distinction is, a chicken breathing which voices a vowel is making something vibrate; maybe it's how that vibration starts which contributes to the grain. Perhaps it is a little unsteady as it begins to vibrate, because so little pressure is applied. Especially if it's not deliberate.

Be it here parenthesized that the turkey, otherwise beyond the scope of this document, makes a noise like a chicken who has swallowed some Paisley.

To conclude: it would be stupid to deny that there is a difference between silence and the sound of chickens. However much the state and composition of the bed may confuse the issue, a river is either running or it is not.

MAGPIES

These birds—for birds they are—have always been phenomenally dangerous, but we have known since antiquity that protection against them is possible. The 'one for sorrow' technique still used today is to count aloud, up to and including the number of magpies present, attaching a word to each, making sure (1) that every odd number and every even number are paired opposites; (2) that all even numbers rhyme.

For instance we find 'two for joy' matched with 'four for a boy', in the most well known version; in another, 'mirth' (two) with 'birth' (four). There is evidence that the first pairing in any spell must be synonyms for 'sorrow' and for 'joy', respectively.

Unfortunately, a rhyme of four is as far as most of the well-known spells work; 'silver' (five) in the common version will keep you safe, if there are five magpies—but if there are six, and the word used is gold, not only does the 'silver'/'gold' pair collapse but the entire spell. It's been suggested that if enough witnesses to a magpie gathering are reciting the rhyme, then the protection is (as it were) split around the group, neutralizing a larger group of magpies piecemeal, in groups of (usually) four.

Researchers have conjectured potential continuations of the rhyme, sometimes as far up as numbers in the twenties. None have been successfully shown to work, but it is an old problem, and like many problems which last a long time, its dead-ends have led to many surprising discoveries along the way.

William Blake was plagued by magpies his entire adult life, and the frequent occurrence of rhymes of 'joy'—particularly with 'boy'—in *Songs of Innocence* and *Songs of Experience* is thought to be directly an artefact of this. 'The Sick Rose' rhymes 'joy' with 'destroy'—it's not known whether verbs are effective, but nobody has discovered a reason why they shouldn't be—and we can also find 'joy' with 'annoy'. There is even in 'Holy Thursday' a rhyme of 'joy' with 'poverty'. It is an attempt at a rhyme easy to forgive if you consider he was probably in fear of his life, facing upwards of ten magpies at the time.

You're probably wondering whether a different starting pair might be fruitful. In the 14th century, nuns at the convent near Ely were working on lists of words rhyming with 'glee', and got considerably further, although above thirty-four they struggled to find convincing pairings of opposites. It's also known that monks in France were working on the problem even earlier. The spell existed all over Europe for centuries before arriving in England.

In fact, magpies have an equivalent spell to protect themselves from a given number of humans, which works according to the same pattern. It is equally effective but far easier to put into practice, since 'joy' in their language rhymes—as does everything—with everything else. This is just one of the reasons they are so dangerous.

PIGEONS

The sound of a pigeon cooing has somehow a direct line to the part of my brain which makes me feel deeply and unbearably sad. It's very strange: it's a nice sound, I like it, but in just a few seconds it makes me feel like I've been waiting, alone, for hours, in the cold and the rain, and have many, many hours more to wait. Waiting for something miserable, as well, like a dentist's appointment, or a replacement bus service to Stevenage. And their sound messes with rain. Rain usually makes me happy. Pigeons are the only sound in the world which makes me dislike rain. I don't even dislike pigeons, particularly.

I wouldn't mind hearing a whole bunch of noisy gulls, like I remember sometimes hearing in Brighton. That was a magic sound. Always made me feel like the sky was massive, which, to be fair, it is. Maybe that's it: gulls doing their massed chaos of *kaaaaaaa*s seem to widen the already vast sky, and to deepen its colours; but the sound of pigeons shrinks the sky, greys it out, and in consequence the world itself becomes extremely small and sterile, a shit suburban promontory: just grey and flat, like the car park round the back of a doctors' surgery. A pigeon under a tree there. Sound and colour from far off cannot reach it. Visible, audible, tangible reality ends a couple of metres away. This is all there is.

I'm bored this afternoon. With the kind of gentle but meaningful hangover to which the sound of pigeons feels indigenous. There's a spider lives on the other side of my window. It would be good if even the smallest of spiders could (rarely, maybe once a year) make at full volume the sound of a gull, or a pigeon. Preferably a gull, but probably a pigeon. Let's move on.

PUFFINS!

'Halfe fysshe, halfe flesshe', according to Thomas Nashe. We know better: these bright-beaked sentinels are 100% bird. We also know that whenever there is a puffin, something nearby is late. Be it a birth, an appointment, the departure of a train, the entry of an orchestral musician, someone due to be interviewed on the radio. Broadly speaking, the more puffins, the more late something is—but it is also true that the more puffins are present, the more things there are nearby which are late. One may get a decent sense of some aggregate of localized delay by counting puffins, but rarely anything specific.

The creature experiencing the delay, it is to be noted, can never see the puffin(s): the latter always happen to be behind a tree or round a corner—even when the former is moving as fast as something which is late is likely to be moving—in what always appears to any observer like an infinitely unlikely accumulation of coincidences; so many broken eye-lines, one after another.

It is not known whether puffins themselves cause delays, or whether puffins are attracted by the presence of delay. More likely, delays and puffins simply are given to occur at the same time according to more or less inscrutable changes in environment, just as do daffodils and lambs in the spring, or flies and wasps in the presence of picnics or rotting fruit. It is conjectured, through impossible to prove, that a puffin arriving late indicates that something nearby is occurring exactly on time. Some ornithologists consider this to be a paradox, but I have never met a paradox, so I don't know what they mean.

STARLINGS

tried to tell me magic wasn't real, via the medium of starling sky-magic. I said, I don't believe you, and they just carried on.

Here's a typo: 'constantly starling'. I made this error when describing the architecture somewhere, and was transported in my imagination to a city of grand sandstone edifices which suddenly and without warning scatter into a hundred thousand black-feathered flecks, all streaming and undulating in lightning-fast murmuration through busy streets of cowering people, only to reassemble just as swiftly as a muscular carved statue adorning a fountain, or as a red-bricked single-storey almshouse set back from the street behind a garden, roses and buddleia still nodding in the air after the flurry, and a few petals drifting to the ground. In general, starlings deserve better than the word 'murmuration'.

SWALLOWS

Two (2) swallows do not make a summer. However, our community is generally in concord in saying that one (1) swallow *does* make a summer. In fact, *any integer number of swallows other than 2* makes precisely one summer.

The reason is as follows: imagine—although you don't need to imagine it, because it's true, if you would only *go and look*—there is some malign sky-ghast hovering by the outcrop there, which in a single inhalation exactly halves any swallow population which can be halved without remainder, the sound of tearing or snapping and a shower of small bones from above, nothing else visible then a chaos of scatter and alarm and a sad mound of survivors.

In a summer made of a massive even number of swallows this sky-ghast may for reasons unknown destroy a huge number of swallows. That this loss is devastating emotionally is compounded when we consider that the resulting number of swallows whether even or odd in all cases except that of a single pair still 'makes a summer', following the axioms.

A massive odd number of swallows may seem to be safe, but we must take care to remember that swallows may die individually by other means; it is to be hoped that the sky-ghast is absent or distracted when one of an odd number of swallows dies, leaving the assembled birds in an even quantity.

Now suppose the apparition again, and again, of the sky-ghast, feasting on a summer comprised of a swallow population which is a power of two, until finally the number of swallows making the summer is 32, then 16, then 8, and then 4, and then at last 2. A tragedy for the swallow population, made worse by the fact that it is no longer summer. Wouldn't the summer be salvaged, seems the obvious question, if the sky-ghast just halved this population?

One (1) swallow does make a summer, after all. Unfortunately, the very instant there are two (2) swallows, the sky-ghast itself perishes, for sky-ghasts can only survive in the summer. We've all seen one, as it devoured its final brace. Do you not remember? Immediately as autumn fell it faded.

Yes, it is some small consolation that there are survivors among the swallows, and we may hope that those two swallows are very much in love with each other. But it is definitely no longer summer.

If you must make a summer, make it with an odd number of swallows. Experts in summer are studying swallow populations one less than a power of two. Experts in sky-ghasts are studying autumn.

LAGAN

60 Chalk and electricity

In Liverpool Anglican Cathedral there is a 2008 work of art. Ten words of illuminated text, as if handwritten:

I Felt You And I Knew You Loved Me

The glass of the lettering glows in bright pink neon, blazing out under a stained-glass window.

Liverpool Metropolitan Cathedral, the Catholic one, feels when you stand in it like a vast cylindrical vault, with no internal membrane or floor separating it from its conical roof. My memory, all these years later, has retained the sounds and the feelings of standing inside that building better than it has the sights. What follows is visual, so you may expect it to be wrong.

Spaced around the dark grey concrete of that immense circular wall are fourteen stained glass windows, one for each station of the cross. Each is a very thin strip, a narrow rectangle of bright red glass, set into the concrete, running from floor to ceiling, like the gap between two columns of text, illuminated in preparation for a deity to inhabit it. I say 'very thin': they are each several yards wide. When the sun hits these windows directly, they glow as if from another universe. They are astonishingly powerful.

It was the first and only piece of architecture which has ever made me start crying. It was a gorgeous surprise, doing that. I was not feeling fragile; I was not expecting it at all. Those windows, those vertical bars of illuminated deep-red glass, filamentous but colossal, were overwhelming. Something was overwhelming, anyway: I have done just enough research to know that my architectural memory is wrong.

One New Year's Day, in Brighton, I saw something breathtaking. I was feeling fragile, and hungover, and I was with a hungover companion, who was also feeling fragile. We went for a walk around Hanover, including a visit to the ducks and geese in the park, and we forlornly loped away from an off-license which we had not expected to be closed. Suddenly we were at the northern end of Windmill Street, looking seaward. The offshore windfarm seemed to be poking out above the building in front of the horizon like a garden of spiky, brittle, ivory weathervanes. We tried to take photographs, but they didn't come out.

Then, at about ten minutes before sunset, some clouds must have cleared as we watched, because the sun, forever angling itself a little differently, lit up the stems of the wind turbines in an electric neon pink. It was stunning. For a second I thought I was thinking of Virginia Woolf's use of 'bars' and 'lines' in the dawn seascape which opens *The Waves*. Perhaps I was.

Then I realised, more definitely, that I was thinking of two buildings I hadn't visited in a decade. From one, a memory of the colour: the bright neon of that artwork in Liverpool Anglican Cathedral. Suddenly, here it was, as if the rest of some numinous tub of helium paint had been unearthed, and had been used to streak the white uprights of the turbines.

From the other, from Liverpool Metropolitan Cathedral, a memory to fit their shapes: these columns hovering over the sea, glowing there so brightly, recalled the stained glass windows—those 'thin vertical bars' that had so overwhelmed me, whatever they actually are in reality.

With a diagram on the winter sky some cosmic benevolence, this is what it looked like, had wished to remind the surface-dwellers of flamingos, but had only chalk and electricity to hand.

61 Solar mill

The night was winter in his roughest mood;
The morning sharp and clear. But now at noon
Upon the southern side of the slant hills,
And where the woods fence off the northern blast,
The season smiles, resigning all its rage,
And has the warmth of May. The vault is blue
Without a cloud, and white without a speck
The dazzling splendour of the scene below.

William Cowper, *The Task*
Book VI. 'The Winter Walk At Noon'

It was that kind of a day. Winter, but it might have been summer. From our window London dazzled too, in its way; it looked like it had a special splendour to it that day, this city we had never fallen out of love with, but which we both now had to leave. There had indeed been a little snow, hours earlier, but it was almost entirely vanished by the middle of the day.

It was the same time of year as I'm writing now, between Christmas and New Year: that unaccountable little catenary in the calendar, when the rigid envelope of days grows soggy, and reality takes the opportunity to smear and clamber over itself in a gentle chaos of hangovers and dismal anticipation.

We'd broken up, my boyfriend and I. Not for any bad reason; for good ones, in fact, and in as good a way as could be hoped for. Our lives were going in different directions—his, to a job on another continent—and we had discussed it all at length, and managed, anomalously for us, never to bicker about it. By October-time we had accepted what to do, with both optimism and sadness. I confess I think we both secretly felt we had been 'very grown-up' about it, between us. And this, our last day, not that either of us could bring ourselves to say so, felt exactly like the bright wintry weather: a sort of gladdening contradiction.

The week just gone had hosted several 'lasts' of ours; we had been deliberate about that. Christmas had been our last one together, and we had made a lavish game of treating it as such. On Boxing Day, we'd gone on our favourite long walk for the last time. Both had been a little tearful, but the tears had been brief, and somehow nourishing. The previous evening, by chance, we had spotted that something which we both were in the mood for was on BBC1 at 8pm, so we had agreed on it as our last 'watch TV with cheap wine from the shop together', enjoying how daft it felt. In fact, when was the last time I sat down at a particular time, to watch something on broadcast television?

The night before—this was the idea, anyway—we had fucked 'for the last time'. That stupid idea failed as a 'last' because when we woke up in the morning we immediately wanted to fuck again; and that was, obviously, even more fun, because we were supposed to be in a great deal of a hurry, so it was not allowed, or at least was not sensible; and, also, because repeatedly on the very brink of getting up we had instantly melted into deciding: let's fuck again. Eventually we tumbled downstairs and into the kitchen, me wearing his pants, because he had made a point of stealing my dressing gown, because it was cold, and because he always did think being annoying was funny (he was usually right). There we assembled a hasty and, from what we had planned, drastically attenuated 'last breakfast' together. The sun jangled in, and the surface of everything was bright and happy. Yes, happy, and not even falsely so.

All this minor but careful ceremony was part of an effort to make what were in truth sad events—impossible not to recognize individually as final shared moments, of so many different kinds—into little mutual gifts to each other. It had been lovely. It was going well. But we were pushed for time, we had to finish packing, and the sense of tautly maintained tenderness began to fray a little. The day became boring, and increasingly stressful. Most of the furniture had gone yesterday; only the bed, and an annoying, unwieldy bureau, belonged to the flat. It was a shell of a place now. My stuff was in a pile of boxes in the living room, and it was, with me, going to stay in the flat for a few lonely days. His stuff was boxed up in the corridor, near the front door; it was all going to go into a van in a couple of hours, where it would be driven, with him, to his parents' house in

Kent. There, tomorrow, it would be unpacked, and re-sorted, into stuff that was staying in England, and stuff that was accompanying him across the Atlantic in a few weeks' time.

The process of collecting and securing and then storing the very last layers, in a flat you're vacating, of the very last of all your shite, the most annoying objects of all, the bits left over when all the serious and obvious packing has been done, is the bit that really seems to take forever: we both knew this, from experience, and we were pissed off with ourselves, and with each other, for having left ourselves so little time to deal with it all. It takes even longer when the objects (rather than just the labour) have to be distributed between two people, which we should also have seen coming. Once, a year or two ago, he'd given to the debris at the bottom of a bag of Bombay Mix the name 'crilt', or 'the crilt layer', and it felt today like our hands were busy with the insane task of trying to sift, even to organize, the thin film of crilt left by our own lives, the most dusty and stupid artefacts of a relationship, conducted in a place, for a duration. When I voiced this, he got irritable—he didn't remember the word, even though it had been his invention.

It was not even all our own stuff, of course it wasn't: there was an inexplicable landline telephone, there were ornaments which belonged to neither of us, there were big floppy course textbooks about management; at one point we discovered a grey corrugated tube, a hefty one, which a cat could easily have crawled through. There was a cat toy, which we had to stop to play with and giggle at—it was a plastic ring, the size of a potty, on top of which was fitted a spring; and on top of the spring was a fluffy white blob, with eyes and ears, a bit like a mouse, which darted and bounced about. It was brilliant.

Behind where the TV had been, there were cobwebs, and old useless cables going in and out of badly-made holes; there were sheets of stickers, the kind you used to get with VHS tapes, and among all this a slightly crumpled grey cardboard box. Three inches by three inches, and maybe six inches tall. Inside it was a transparent glass bulb, the size of an apple, which tapered in and then out to a base; it was made of very delicate glass, and the base seemed to be taut, a flaring of the glass with a sheet of paper stretched over it and padded with a layer of thin felt. Obviously this was the end on which you were supposed to put it down, on a surface, although in the box this curious object had been upside down.

Inside the bulb was a central rod, about which were wobbling four square vanes, set diagonally and attached by one corner. They were made of something very thin, and each was black on one side and white on the other. They also looked as if they ought to spin about the central rod, but there was no switch, and certainly no room for any batteries. It was a brittle glass globe, with fragile bits inside, and that was it.

Yes, we were in a hurry, but when a rubbish dusty corner of the flat offered us this mysterious object, the afternoon's mood changed a little, as it suddenly seemed to invite us to treat it a bit like the discovery of treasure. We did not get too excited, because we had so much packing still to do, but it was fun to be distracted by a strange device for a moment. Soon enough we dredged approximations of its image from our memories, and identified it as, well, we hadn't the first idea—but it was 'the kind of thing they sell at the Science Museum', wasn't it?

That would have to do, unfortunately; we had dog-eared documents to ram into carrier bags, without even attempting to sort them, and quarter-full, disappointed-looking bottles of shampoo and shower gel to collect or to throw away. The Science Bulb didn't belong to either of us, that was certain. If we had returned it to its box immediately, we might have discovered the little leaflet in the box, and got a name for our discovery: SOLAR RADIOMETER, it would say, when eventually we did find it, in bold capitals with rounded corners, noting at the start of a long paragraph of tiny grey text that it was also known as a 'light mill', or 'solar engine'. It did look a bit like a space-age windmill.

We did not find that leaflet until much later, so this mystery glass bulb, which I placed out of the way on a windowsill, lived without a name for three or four hours. Its internal vanes gently started to move, in the winter sun, while the two of us whirled around the flat, oblivious to it.

M

The blue sky over the street outside was darkening; it was between three and four o'clock. We were no longer 'pushed for time': the plan had changed, after a phone call. His dad's van was not starting, something was wrong, and the journey that took us away from each other would not be tonight after all. We had a little crisis, between us, but the initial panic subsided when we realised together that this was no disaster. No plans were disrupted as a consequence. In fact, all that it meant now was that we had one more night together! Our packing would still be finished today, but not in a hurry. Whatever happened, it occurred to me that we would be very hungry when we were done, and we would perhaps not have much energy to cook. Not only that, we'd have very little to cook with. It was mostly in boxes. I suggested a takeaway, and inevitably this idea became our 'one last takeaway'. One more night together felt like a free gift from the universe, and a takeaway to celebrate was the most obvious thing in the world.

Perhaps this was not a good idea. I had been explicit in the past about my belief that among the most joyous meals it's possible to have are those takeaways which you get, exhausted, the evening you first move into a new place, eaten off knees while sat on boxes, when you are excited about the coming weeks and months—and, if you have moved in with someone, excited for this new stage in your relationship. Except for the boxes, and the fact it was a takeaway, this meal would be the opposite of that in every respect.

We pushed some bigger boxes against one wall and I grabbed the duvet to put over them. This, tonight, would be a sofa. In front of the 'sofa' we dragged some more boxes, forming a low table. On an impulse I grabbed the bulb from the windowsill—its vanes will not have been spinning now, because darkness had fallen—and I grandly placed it on one of the boxes off of which we planned to eat our dinner, as if it was an ornate candlestick, or as if I was a chess grand-master playing a magnificent move. I sat a little too heavily on the pretend sofa, folded my arms, and looked at the bulb.

—What is it?

That's when he looked inside the bulb's box, correctly suspecting I might have not noticed if there was something else there. The leaflet got caught; he pulled it out awkwardly, with a scratchy sound, and in a booming voice he read:

—'**SOLAR RADIOMETER**'!

He made a silly, wide-eyed face at the bulb—the **SOLAR RADIOMETER**—and resumed reading in a phony American accent, mimicking the tone and emphasis of a 1950s information film:

—'The **SOLAR RADIOMETER**,' *Tim*, 'also known as the *solar mill*, demonstrates with *simple physics* how *light* can be *transformed* into energy...'

The vanes probably had been spinning all afternoon, but we hadn't noticed. It most definitely was the kind of thing they sell at the Science Museum. The leaflet warned that fluorescent light wouldn't work, but that was fine: we hadn't one of them anyway. Natural light was best, okay, but we'd missed that, okay, but what if we tried lamps, well, the one lamp we hadn't packed away, oh, unless—have you got a lighter?

—What?

—Fire is natural light, isn't it.

—No way will that be enough.

—What this (pointing at the leaflet) is calling 'natural light' is a *fire*, right? The sun is a fire.

—A *massive* fire...!

Somehow, over the next half an hour, packing was finished. At last. We opened a couple of beers and resumed being silly about the solar radiometer. I ripped open a sealed box, because I knew it was where the last of my candles were, and I forcefully shoved the base of one into an empty beer bottle from last night so that we could have a candlelit dinner. Our curry would still be another fifty minutes, since we had finished packing sooner than we expected.

He went digging in some recently-sealed boxes for crockery, and while he did, I decided that the solar radiometer could sit on our 'table'—or could sit somewhere, at least, propped up next to the flame of the candle. I experimented with putting it back on the windowsill, and then in several other places too. It could be our evening's entertainment.

Smiling at me, a quiet hiss of a laugh escaping through his nose at the absurdity of what I was doing, he padded over, bent his grin into a mocking frown, and wrapped his hands gently over my shoulders, so that I turned round to look at him; we communicated silently and happily for a couple of seconds, like nuzzling animals. He kissed me lingeringly on the back of my neck, sat down, and opened another beer. I followed, bringing the beer-bottle candlestick and the radiometer back to our makeshift dining-table.

—Right.

He withdrew a lighter from his back trouser pocket, and, lifting the beer bottle at an angle, flicked a flame, readying to light the wick. For some reason I picked up the radiometer, as if it too needed to be held close to the flame.

I've no idea what happened, or how it happened. There was a barely audible pop, and in my hand a sudden puddle of broken glass. Some tiny triangles of glinting debris landed quietly on the cardboard box. The vanes were loose on my palm, no longer at right angles to each other. It looked pathetic, like a broken violin, all its vital tautness and precision lost in a tangled catastrophe. There must from somewhere have come a tiny amount of water, inexplicably, which was soaking now into the cardboard of our pretend dinner-table, turning it dark and soft below the shards.

For both of us, this broke the spell. We were hungry, we were a little bit drunk, we were definitely 'over-tired', we were at the very end of our relationship, and we had somehow broken this inexplicable thing, the miserable day's only nice surprise. We started sobbing and did not stop. We couldn't stop. We were inconsolable. We hated everything. Inconsolable and ruined and angry. Nothing was fair. Ugly, gasping, hiccuping crying, the sort that physically hurts, and covers your face and hands in tears and snot. They were truly horrible tears, and we weren't even able to hug, or to help each other through it, because that only reminded us what we were about to lose.

We were like infants who wail because they have just badly damaged a favourite toy, and who know—whatever faith they have in the world, or the people in it—who know, without the slightest hope of their being wrong, that this object can never be fixed. This thing is broken, forever. It is ended.

62 Fluid

Staring at this object on the windowsill I have been trying to recall words which describe fluid. They have each arrived with their own surprising new image, like emoji-fast grapes popping off vines: 'brackish', 'limpid', 'pellucid'. They all have some sharp tang or edge; I want to say they're all 'a bit much'. Not one, so far, is fit for purpose. Some of them seem to come with extra information: how salty or how inland is the fluid may turn out to matter in ways I would need to check.

The fluid I am staring at is magical, for sure. It is, literally and precisely, 'limey', but that word is taken. The fluid is, in a way, inaccessible. The fluid is a mystery. It is transparent. It is also yellow, or golden. It's neither, really, but both approximate it.

The fluid is in an attractive, hexagonal glass jar on my windowsill. The lid is brass-coloured and could do with a clean; it has a layer of stubborn dust which as evidenced by a streak is gunky, presumably because of an oily or sticky film on the surface. Inside the glass jar is a halved lime, or, more accurately, the two rounded ends of a lime which has had just one or two slices removed from it. Both are 'facing' the same way (approximately south-east, I think, but it's possible to rotate the jar).

I was living in a different house when the limes went in the jar. The entire assemblage is the result of my having made two glasses of gin and tonic, one evening. I put what remained of the lime, which was most of it, in this jar. I do not know why. I also do not know why I had an attractive hexagonal glass jar with a brass-coloured lid in my bedroom, nor what had been in it. Nor do I know why it was empty. Once the limes were in it, it found its way to hiding behind a picture frame on my desk. The jar and I forgot each other again, for a time. When we were re-united, it was spring.

For some reason, I decided to put the jar somewhere it would get a lot of sunlight. In the bottom of the jar, now that a lot of time has passed, is the fluid. About eight millimetres. I have now moved house with it four times, and every time it has gone somewhere sunny. It first struck me after eight months of sunlight, warmth, condensation, whatever had been going on, how beautiful that fluid was. My feeling is that the fluid has been patiently coaxed from the limes, rather than 'extracted' from it.

The limes—I'm going, I think, to keep referring to the two halves of one lime as if they are separate limes, in the plural—the limes themselves after a few months looked like lemons—(ditto?)—and at this late stage they have lost hue enough to 'look grey', if it is reasonable to say of something which doesn't look grey that it looks grey: certainly they strike as less colourful than I feel they ought to be. I think if you believed it was lemons (which is to say: a lemon) in the jar, they would not look as grey as they look given the knowledge that they are limes.

It was obvious to me after just a few months that I will never deliberately open that jar, so I imagine the fluid it contains to be a magical distillation, with important but unknowable properties. I might wonder whether it is to be drunk, or its vapours inhaled. Do the gods like it? Perhaps it can assist in spells. Good spells, of course. I'm not sure it could ever be used malevolently: look at it. It's too vital.

At this point I'm not sure whether the amount of fluid will ever increase. Perhaps the limes have—the lime has—nothing left to give. The halves are beautiful, but are to be respected, like the detached caps of some beige, super-deadly Amanita, one whose warning isn't nearly as bright as the fly agaric's.

M

It is important to me—and I think of it every time I look at the jar—that the world in which it was sealed shut, the depths of that winter, is a world in which K was still alive. I wonder how the contents of that jar, that magical fluid in particular, would react on being released into a world which is now so destitute of him. Most likely not in any way detectable or comprehensible to us. But you understand why I say the fluid is inaccessible. I can open that jar, but I can't.

63 The sea

Last night I went to the beach. For the first time in forever, to the very edge of the sea. It was riddled with ghosts, and I was perturbed by it: I felt tense, on guard, unsettled, almost upset, and not sure where to look, nor for how long, like a cat on bonfire night.

The tide must have been going out, because just before the sea began, a ridge of pebbles kept back a long, thin, shallow lagoon, stretching as far east as you could see, whose surface was completely still, such that it reflected the moonlight unbroken, in a bright haunted strip.

A man not fifteen yards away was performing some kind of magic, limbs flailing; he seemed to be becoming something else. I had come to this part of town to suck dick, but that route through the bushes had seemed uncharacteristically deserted, and I had quickly found the ghostly sea itself too compelling to resist. Yet immediately it frightened me, and very soon I found it impossible to stay.

Being back on the land—by which I just mean no longer on the beach, but it really had felt like being out at sea—I felt immediately better, and far, far safer—that's it, that's the word, I had felt unsafe—yet I kept looking seaward as I walked.

A large grey shape was visible, back on the beach, obscure and difficult to see, but seemingly a person. It was so motionless, every single time I looked back, that I found myself fixing my gaze on it as I walked. It was inhumanly still. For a minute I walked without taking my eyes off it.

It can't have been a person. It must have been part of the architecture of whatever that object was nearby, some sort of shed. Immediately as I made this decision the figure raised its left arm to its face. A single movement, and a new pose held. The shock of it was enough to make me gasp out loud. From then on, I walked quicker.

I love the sea. I have always trusted it, and believed in it as some sort of final sanctuary. And over the years it has been very good to me. But on this occasion, I was not welcome. It was extraordinary to feel with such vividness and such certainty that the sea did not want me there, that I was being warned.

64 Moonlight, reflected

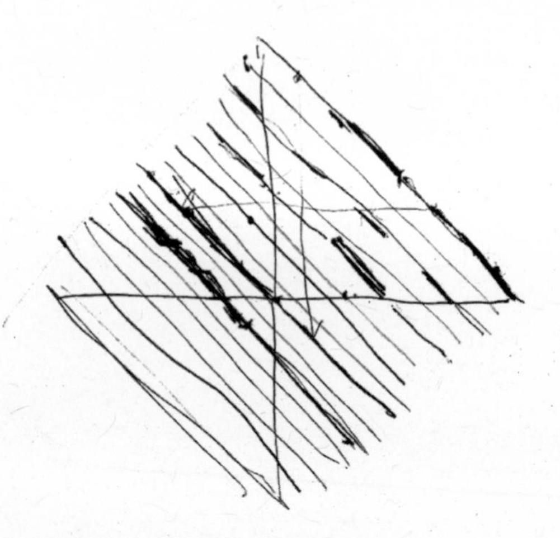

The sound of a pin dropping is scarcely audible.

The sound of a pin landing is audible but not
remarkable.

Less remarkable at any rate than the conditions for
hearing it.

The sound of a coin landing is likewise not
remarkable.

The sound of a coin dropping is scarcely audible.

Not unless the fall is broken, or broken up.

At the very bottom of a cave there was nobody.

The sound of the moon lighting is audible, but it is
not audible to us.

Not even if it's broken, or broken up.

The sound of the moon lighting is beautiful.

Very rarely, when the moon lights on the right rock,
a coin breaks off.

At the very top of a cave the moon once lighted on a
rock.

Into the cave broke off a coin.

The rest of the moon went lighting into the sea.

The cave was deep, and full of twists and turns.

A tangle of dark tunnels snaking down,
under the cliffs.

Somebody at the very bottom could never have seen
sunlight, or moonlight.

Somebody at the very bottom could never have
heard the coin which broke off when the moon
lighted on a rock, not to begin with.

At the very bottom of the cave there was nobody.

Coins broken off from moonlight have, in the past,
been called treasure, although they have nothing
whatsoever to do with money or wealth.

On the very other side of the sea were ghosts.

We hear the sound of the moon lighting only if it
breaks off a coin whose fall in turn is broken,
or broken up.

Ghosts hear the sound of the moon lighting,
interrupted by the silences of it being broken,
or broken up.

Somebody at the bottom of the cave might have
begun to hear the coin falling, as the fall was
broken, or broken up.

A ghost on the other side of the sea, as the sea broke
up the moon lighting, might have begun to hear
it, to find it beautiful, before it was broken, or
broken up, into a silence.

As it bounced, deeper and deeper, somebody at the
very bottom of the cave might have heard the
coin, sounding louder and louder.

At the very bottom of the cave was nobody.

Moonlight is sometimes said to be sunlight, reflected.

This makes as much sense as the idea that the sound
of a coin landing is moonlight, stopped.

The sound of a coin bouncing down a deep cave falls
on our ears at the same speed, approximately,
as ghosts on the very other side of the sea hear
the moon lighting through it.

The sea changes faster than the moon lights.

Coins which break off when the moon lights on a
rock are slower than moonlight.

Compared to the speed of coins, let alone to the
speed of moonlight or the sea, caves change so
slowly that they may as well be fixed.

Often, on the other side of the sea, the sound of the
moon lighting gets brighter and brighter.

The ghosts there hear it, and they find it beautiful,
but the sea will always change, and the sound
of the moon lighting through it will always be
broken, or broken up.

Just once, the moon lighted on a rock, a coin broke
off, fell into the sea, and went all the way
through, to the very other side.

The ghost who had heard the moon lighting found the coin and found it beautiful.

Ghosts are not always visible.

It has been conjectured that when they make themselves visible, ghosts reflect moonlight brightest of all, brighter than anything else.

In this sense, a ghost, if we can see it, is mimicking the wearing of a hi-viz garment.

There are many conjectures built on the assumption this is true.

All would topple if it were false.

One is the idea that there are many more ghosts at sea than those we can see, and that those we do see are undertaking some kind of repair work, or inspection.

Another is the idea that a ghost becoming invisible may suggest that the peril of its crossing the sea has passed.

Another is the conjecture that crossing the sea in either direction is just as unsafe for ghosts whether we can see them or not.

There is no question that they are highly skilled.

Perhaps what they are repairing is the sea.

Perhaps what they are inspecting is the moon, and
the sea's capacity for reflecting it.

M

We know that ghosts navigate the sea by debris. It was conjectured a century and a half ago, and proved in the 1960s, that ghosts distinguish 163 species of wreckage. Only four of the broadest categories have made their way into our understanding. We call them *flotsam*, *jetsam*, *lagan*, and *derelict*.

These four designations are written into our maritime laws, but they are directional, like points on a compass, and they are like a tarot deck. As with our famous humours, they are, singularly and in combination, descriptors of character, condition, or fate.

Each species of wreckage is represented by a symbol or sigil, derived from a constellation in our night sky. Our night sky is the same one ghosts see.

Flotsam and *jetsam* are wreckage arriving in grains. They float, which means they are attracted to the surface on our side of the sea. They are perilous to navigate by, because they change with the sea, which changes quicker than the moon lights. *Jetsam* is wreckage which has been jettisoned. This means we have deliberately discarded it. *Jetsam* is intended as wreckage; *flotsam* is simply wreckage.

Lagan and *derelict* are shipwreck. They have more size. They sink, which means they are attracted to the surface on the very other side of the sea. Either, and sometimes both at once, may function as a lodestone of the sea-bed, and further distort the moon lighting through the already changing sea.

Lagan is shipwreck on the sea-bed which has been marked with a buoy. This means we have decided it is, despite everything, not gone forever.

Derelict is shipwreck which is irretrievable, lost forever to the very other side of the sea. We borrow its name and use it pejoratively. What the ghosts of the sea teach us is that something we abandon forever on the very other side of the sea may gain as much as it loses. The rich and strange magic of being consigned to unimpeded sea-change, and with that to an eternity of the moon lighting, of breaking the moon lighting's fall, or breaking it up.

None of us has ever heard moonlight from the very other side of the sea. Nor can we imagine it, from our side of the sea. We misunderstand the moon lighting, and the sea changing; we think it harms shipwreck. We understand harm well enough, because we are often harmful ourselves, and often deliberately. Ghosts can be harmful, deliberately. The moon can be harmful, but not deliberately.

Coins go missing, possibly because of the moon lighting. Caves disappear, possibly because of the sea changing. Only we could have supposed that the sea is in poor condition and in need of repair. It is more likely that ghosts are simply maintaining the sea, in a way we have shown we cannot.

By the changing of the sea the moonlighting of all manner of wreckage is broken, or broken up. It is supposed to be. Even when no wreckage is present, which is very rare, by the changing of the sea the lighting of the moon is broken, or broken up.

Seen from either side, and even in the dark, the changing of the sea is moonlight, reflected.

We can conjecture, given that the changing of the sea is moonlight, reflected, yet it can still appear completely dark, that the sea is full of ghosts reflecting moonlight but choosing not to make themselves visible.

65 The sea, again

The last time I went down to the sea, it was gone midnight. Lots of very weird shit was going on. I told you about it. It was absolutely haunted. I got the very strong feeling that it did not want me there, that I did not belong at whatever ceremony it was arranging that night. So I left it, and its company of creatures.

Yesterday, down by the marina, I was walking with someone along the sea wall. For some reason, in the moment of distributing between us some Fisherman's Friends, I spontaneously felt it would be appropriate to do so three ways. I said it, aloud:

—One for you... one for me... and one for the sea...

And with this I tried to fling one far enough to get it beyond the massive fortifications of the marina arm. But the wind was too strong, and the Fisherman's Friend was dragged back, and landed on the concrete.

Immediately a great crashing wave flung over, out from the tide, and the sea grabbed its lozenge after all. It feels like we might be on good terms again.

66 Queer, powerful things

for *not here: a queer anthology of loneliness* (2017)

Dear Richard,

Thank you for putting this together, from one queer and often lonely man to another. I've included two poems, I guess they're pretty lonely, but I'd like to submit this letter as well; it's a reworked attempt, at last, to describe a particular kind of loneliness, which I'm grateful not to have experienced in a long while, a fraught and hectic and acute kind. I'm remembering that silently devastating experience of language-loss which you go through when your time with a lover must come to an end: or rather it isn't loss, it is the delay of a loss, which is maybe the point, what hurts is the delay, because that tiny, intimate, beautiful little linguistic eddy of in-jokes and shared tics isn't so suddenly and comprehensively abrupted out of your life in the same way as are certain tangible things (your ex-lover's body, their clothes, their stuff), or certain places (their room, their favourite haunts, the place you usually met them after work), and so on, because those were things you came to recognize, and with which you became for better or worse familiar, and their absence or their interdiction is kind of immediate, because you get to redraw each other's maps, practically (returning each other's keys) and personally (deciding to avoid places, if only for a while)—all of which is very different from your shared little pocket-idiolect, you know, *your* argot, because you made that together, without ever really meaning to, over however long a time it was, and by the time you're aware of it, it's already become instinctual, and the time you're most aware of it is when all of a sudden you can't use it any more, and seriously if you could just switch it off then the blank glassy few weeks after a breakup would be a great deal less fucking hurtful, because you know what happens, for a while now you will be walking down the street or sat in a café and something will make your brain leap at the potential for a particular kind of wordplay, and then you will be silent, and very, very alone for a few seconds, because there is nobody else who speaks that little language; and then you will find yourself thinking these things less and less, because they are like a bad shock every time, they just hurt so much, and the bits of you that unvolitionally make the jokes you made with your lover or speak the way you spoke with your lover are slowly cowed into submission like a dog kicked in the face every time it barks, and eventually perhaps after a few weeks you will remember with upsetting distance a kind of pun that you used to make together, and you will realize that the tiny loops and pools of language and jargon and in-joke you made together are at last on the way to having atrophied and died, and honestly: it breaks my heart, or, it has broken my heart, more than once, whether shattered it or fractured it along a plane or however else. But I've been so glad though to find that hearts, once retrieved from the rainy, sluggy compost bin they sometimes end up in, are actually queer, powerful things, which won't be ruined or got rid of that easily, capable even if it takes an age of new languages with new lovers and new life.

That's more than enough, isn't it. I hope you're well; I love you, I'll see you soon, let's make some more things together. x

67 This one word (a free translation)

This one word as it drifts conscious staggered by gentle blinks has been dreaming, perhaps of nights where the sun never sets, or of days where it never rises; it has been oversleeping much lately, this icy chandelier of a word; it is dreamt, it is real; it is polysynthetic, tangles of vivid meaning barely visible beyond the fog, hovering above and yet indigenous to the tundra; flickering bars dot the sight of it; perhaps as it packs in and swirls through what in English would be an entire paragraph's worth of text—this paragraph, specifically—this one word burrows in under the ice and urgently prepares for an increase of intensity in the surrounding perpetual winter, the whole place drifting conscious and buffered by gentle steppes: this one word is a tiny dormouse of a word, purposefully shrinking and moss-lining its immediate environment toward a safe point-source of absolute reassurance; it is complex and tinctured, full of itself, a bottle of self-weaving semantic wicker, DNA curling right back into itself; this one word is a single Paisley, in a cosmos where such patterns are creatures, dropping out of the visible spectrum as it spirals away and does something unreasonable and quantum; perhaps now, its morning long since over with and its afternoon fading fast, you and this one word could cook something luxuriantly chaotic together in an unshared kitchen, subject to no time constraints, or otherwise indulge that latter fact by putting the oven on low and leaving something inside while you and this one word go for a walk together which ends in a pub with a fire: a dreamt, tangled fire, the sight of which this one word, itself dotted with bars, dots with bars, as if they are a preparatory sketch for the lines which show the brickwork on a cartoon igloo, or as if they are an entire paragraphs' worth of text—this paragraph, specifically—more and more of its words magicked before your eyes into dashes—come on in, my friend, is where this one word arrives, free at last of its worries and anxieties: it is cold outside, evening, and time for dinner.

68 Rockpools, oaks

These two words represent something I knew once, for half a second, a brief revelation which I owe entirely to a friend. I will try to explain.

It happened in 1986, when I was living in the Sussex countryside. He almost fell through the gate, dashing and stumbling from a taxicab, and cowering from a thunderstorm. It was toward the middle of winter. I had been looking forward to his visit so much that I was at my front door as soon as the cab pulled up. It was late, because the trains had been chaos, and the skies had got darker than I was ever used to because the night was somehow moonless. There were flickers of lightning, from between sooty clouds; the electrical heart of the storm must have been miles distant, but the rain was so heavy and relentless that you could only laugh at it. The raindrops felt incredibly young, somehow: vigorous, triumphant, and as fat as grapes.

My friend held a soaking wet newspaper above his head, ridiculously, in the absence of an umbrella, as he hauled his overnight bag and I scurried down the path to meet him. He looked superbly handsome by the light of my torch, which rattled. The power had been out for a few hours. I shouted—'Look at you!' I think it was—and then gabbled that he looked like he'd swum 'down' two seas, whatever that meant. Something transmitted between us faster even than the flickers in the sky confirmed that our friendship, after so many years, was still intact and ineffable, and his splendid face, dripping with rain, joined mine in a broad, happy grin.

I pushed him inside, and the tiles on the floor were immediately drenched. We embraced gorgeously. I scurried to find some towels, hopefully they would be warm, I said, and I pointed him to where he would be sleeping, and started talking about dry clothes he could put on. Oh and there's an enormous dressing gown on the door, I said. It's like a great grizzly bear! He ignored the mention of dry clothes, but was immediately excited about the dressing gown, and tumbled upstairs to find it.

I peered out through the open door. The grumbling air pulsed and twitched brightly in the distance, like the wingtip of a snapped bird. I shut it out. My friend got himself warm and dry. I knocked over and re-lit a candle, one of eleven I'd dotted about the living room. One had dropped and rolled underneath something before I'd managed to place it anywhere. I poured each of us an extravagant measure of my most expensive brandy, which was not very expensive.

It was a wonderful, reassuring evening. We enjoyed each other's company joyfully and fluently, as if it was the very thing at which we were both most expert, just as we had years ago. I tried to speak French, but I was hopeless; his English was as perfect as it always had been. Long before I had known him, before our paths crossed, he had travelled a great deal, and had sharpened early an instinct for languages of which I was intensely jealous. Ten months, usually, it took him to get solidly comfortable in some new tongue, however hard it was reputed to be, so long as he actually lived among its speakers. I have no language but this one, the one I grew up in.

It took us three hours to notice the significant fact that our preferences for facial hair, since the last time we had met, had swapped over exactly. We were so happy that we found this funnier than it really was, and we knew that we did, which in turn we found funnier than it really was, and this subsided into a hectic period of about three minutes in which absolutely everything was funny; we were all hiccups and donkeyish noises, and actual physical pain.

For most of the night, nothing we spoke about had anything to do with why I have decided to set this down—so I will skip ahead, until just before three in the morning. Whenever (and whatever) is the witching hour, we chatted, drank, and smoked through it, content enough to be completely oblivious to any ghouls or ghosts, any emissaries from the whipping weather which might have wanted to get in. It began when my friend poured himself a fifth or sixth whisky, sat back with his arms folded without touching it, paused, and simply said my name.

He called me 'Tim', not 'Timothy', which was unusual for him. I looked back, friendly and expectant.

Even through a fug of alcohol I was aware that he was being careful about something, suddenly recalibrating alone the mood of the room; it had, til then, been such a collaborative atmosphere. I went with it. He asked if he could tell me something. Something that had been bothering him. Naturally I said, Of course, go on. It might be difficult to explain, he said.

He had, he said, been disturbed by a kind of persistent hallucination. It was, and this was the trouble he had in explaining it, not a hallucination *of* anything. It was an absence, rather than a presence. The problem, the idea, the initial spark, had not been his own. It had come from a dream, a dream which a colleague, or perhaps a student, had shared with him, an incredibly long time ago—a dream which all these years later he had had for himself. Both the dream and its repetition were of the nature of a revelation, one which threatened to become a waking obsession. The dream, both dreams, were about, or, no, perhaps were, themselves, the discovery of a secret. He repeated himself like this more and more as he went on. Perhaps the secret belonged to nature, or perhaps it belonged to humans. No, he corrected himself impatiently, it definitely belonged to humans. He had been right. It certainly was difficult to explain.

My friend struggled, and it took him several attempts, or perhaps I should call it one long attempt, with rare patches of clarity in which I felt I almost understood. In brief: the secret of the dream, which he carried around with him now, was that certain words have an extra element to them. This extra element is, perversely, missing. Absent.

It is not gone, because it was never there; it cannot have been somehow eroded, or omitted, or amputated, from the word, because it never existed in the first place. To be more specific, certain words—and we are not restricted to any one language—certain words, not all words, but many words, and all of them words of one single syllable, have another syllable preceding them. This preceding syllable is empty. It does not exist and never did. It is silent, though not like a 'silent letter', because those are written. It is not written, and it is not sounded. It is a pulse or a pause of zero duration; it occupies, lasts for, exactly no time. This strange, absent moiety is fully half of the word, yet it is absent... It does precede the syllable we hear, the word we see, written, and it is empty, absent, missing, but the word is not complete without it. If there was not a missing part of the word, coming before it, undetectably, then there would be something missing from the word.

With this tangle I remember him looking at me. It was my turn. Indeed, I did have questions. Which words, for a start? And how could he possibly be aware of something which refused to evidence itself in any way? I tried a gentle joke, but he was not finding things funny. When my friend experienced these syllables, he saw and heard nothing: his imagination refused to conjure false sights or sounds for something which was, as he said a hundred thousand times, not there. But at some level he felt them, was aware of them.

He found that he responded to them as if they were a geology, or perhaps a kind of music: sometimes they felt incredibly vast, they were imaginary filaments of invisible cosmos, the great ridges and walls of gravity which shape the layout of galaxies; sometimes they were tiny, felt in his chest, or behind his back, the way he felt silences or rubato while playing (he was a fine pianist), or in the sudden changes to the tempo of reality while walking beside trees or near a body of still water. Despite the grand similes these hollow but resistant absences, behind or before words he had used his whole life, suddenly and apocalyptically present, were as real to him as bus stops, cats, or the cigarette he was smoking, which at this point he held up before me as if it was proof of its own reality. (I suppose it probably was.) I will stress this point, that this was real to him, not some writerly fancy or academic game: he was upset and frustrated when he could not explain it, or aspects of it, and I felt unkind for initially receiving it all a little flippantly.

We were drunk. He was keen to convey that the manner in which the first, missing halves of these one-syllable words were missing was even harder to explain, or describe, was even more of a problem than the basics of the explanation. The absences were not all alike. They wanted a taxonomy, and, whether he liked it or not, it had fallen to him to imagine his way toward creating one. He compared one such absent foresyllable—the first example he thought of, the nothingness which forms the missing first half of the

English word *tilt*—to the inner shape of a rockpool at high tide, under twelve feet of ocean. Its concavity was not in question; it was the fact that it was unlike the truncated pool which usually fills it: underwater, it had no immediate meniscus, no tangible surface or edge in the reality, or in the substance, in which we might swim around it. He compared another—the absent pulse which precedes and completes the word *long*—to the shock of walking into a room and looking at a blank wall from which a large mirror has just been removed. The shape of that absent hollow space, which was not gone, because it had never been there.

He had not yet written any of this down, or tried to tabulate any possible threads or likenesses between what he was encountering. Deliberately. I would not be the first person, he said, who got obsessed with finding a pattern which maybe can never be found. And here I have a pattern indicated only by things which don't even exist! Yet in his head he had, obviously to me, to both of us, begun to form an irresistible but hopeless schema for his rockpools. Rockpools, and I think it happened that night as we spoke, became his word for them. Many single-syllable words which had an 'ee' vowel sound (however it was notated, and in whatever language and script) had a rockpool which reminded him of the negative space of a seahorse, or perhaps of a Romanesco broccoli bent like it was a small Julia set. In any other circumstance I might have smiled at the description of certain Julia sets as 'small'. I asked about homophones. Their rockpools are different: of course they are, he said, as if it was obvious. *Where*'s rockpool, if anything, seemed to him to be what a moth must imagine to be behind an illuminated bulb; *wear*'s was more like a hollow chamber imagined to sit precisely underneath a kettle. *Whole* has a rockpool akin to a single diamond gap in a chicken-wire fence, once the fence has been removed, but still able to sway in the breeze as if the fence remained. *Hole*, on the other hand, is a complete word, he said. It does not have a rockpool. Nothing is missing. I asked if 'complete' single-syllable words were rare. Yes, they are rare, he said. There are many of them, but they are rare.

I was disturbed by this conversation, especially since I clearly did not and could not share his experience. I asked him to list a few 'complete' words. I felt it might be grounding, somehow. His face was blank, to begin with. *Rare* is one, for a start, he said. Lamp. Lime. Lint. Front. Rook. (A sudden realization.) Rock! *Rock*, of course. *Pool* is not. *Wreck* is one, but not *wrack*. Nor is *rack* with just an 'r'. *Well* is not complete. *Size*—with a z, not the other one. (A long pause.) Beach. Côte. Uh, *rune*. Sown. Ox.

He had slowed down. He smiled at me, as if he had found a good ending, and said, smiling at last, with quiet, lethargic relief: *fox*. Every one of these 'complete' monosyllables had been delivered full of tender care, as if he were sliding them all out at an angle and lovingly re-potting them. Four more times he repeated 'fox', only warped through a yawn, and a visibly good stretch, which I envied and copied.

The drinking, and the extraordinary conversation, had got the better of us. Our speech was hard work, and we were by now barely interrupting a treacle of alternating yawns. The wildly late hour was oscillating through us: he was tired, I was tired, he was tired, I was tired, he was tired. In wobbly concert, as if we were both very, very old, we blew out the remaining five candles before, at last, and it was very, very late, retiring for the night.

M

The dreadful tide of alcohol did not pull me under right away. I lay in bed, cold, hugging the bedding tightly, and more aware that night than ever that I thought in words. I counted my exhalations on the way to sleep, a relic from the worst years of insomnia. I got to *five*, I felt the completed pulse of that word, that single-syllable number, and noticed that every number prior to it was the same. Just one syllable. What if it had a rockpool: what if they all did. How would I know, I thought. How had it not occurred to me to ask about numbers. I imagined writing about what had happened—I imagined telling this story, and even as I thought of the words *as I lay in bed last night*, words of a single syllable felt like straps, or a cage, like ants, or like rain; like situations I could not escape. They were no more just what they were, these words: they ached now with what was, or might be, lost from them, with what I could not see. And the night, not just the night, the whole world was strewn with them, made from them, these strange half things.

Briefly, very briefly, I glimpsed it. What my friend was able to feel, his rockpools, these unreal absences borne by so many words, they suddenly were tangible to me in this moment too. It was scarcely half a second it lasted, but I knew, I absolutely knew, that it was not arbitrary. What I was aware of, in this sliver of the pre-dawn morning, was exactly the same as what my friend now carried around with him all the time. Language laid itself out in grand nets and branches, the tendrils off a reef of coral, the concavities and convexities hidden behind words all real to me now, pulsing and vivifying every thought I had, and every word which came to mind. I tried to visualise them, hoping they would pad the threads in the mesh of language like paired lenses, or bead them like clams' eyes, but they refused to be seen. Of course not, I thought. It's as he said: they are not there.

Opening my own eyes, at the shock of this, dispelling the whole grandeur of it immediately and completely, what I saw then was nothing. Absolute darkness. I do not know whether I had been dreaming. Perhaps I had: perhaps it was the same dream. I must ask my friend, I thought. Tomorrow. I became aware of my breathing, and irritated myself by wondering about the power-cut and its consequences. For some reason I moved my hand in front of my face, experimenting with the dark. I saw nothing. I shut my eyes again and tried to swim among what I had just seen. Perhaps I would not be able to access it again without hearing someone exhaust themselves trying to describe it for three hours. Opening and closing my eyes once more, I wondered whether a word was, to its oak, what an object is to its shadow, in a pitch-dark room.

This new word, from nowhere. Oak. It took a few seconds, but my memory retraced its steps without much conscious effort. My friend, at some point, had said something which I have now looked up and is spelled, in French, *aucune*. Perhaps he was trying it out as a replacement noun for rockpool; perhaps his frustration had become so pure at one point that it splintered out through his first language. It is a word, I now know, to do with absence, or nothing. I remembered that I had needed to unpeg it, at the time, from the memory of a place I had visited as a very young man, since that was clearly not what he had meant.

Now, as I lay in bed, this word, though drastically eroded, was a new name for the secret, for these absent syllables. Any word which previously had a rockpool now just as well had an oak. It meant the exact same thing: an empty syllable, neither heard nor written, and somehow prior to the word as we understand it. I had the image of them growing out of words as if they were invisible leaves, curled at the edges and fronding away into the same nothing they were made of.

The question of whether something was a rockpool or an oak was the same question as whether the absent syllable, as far as the present syllable was concerned, had occurred, or not occurred, *recently* or *lately*. It was the same question, but the answer made no sense. (At the time, I genuinely believed the question made sense.) Rockpools were both *lately* and *recently*, oaks were both *recently* and *lately*; *lately* described both oaks and rockpools, and *recently* described both rockpools and oaks.

I was, definitely, almost asleep. The storm reminded me just how intensely it could wrap the house, how violently it could rattle the windows in its gusts, and I asked—it was reality itself I asked, as if in accidental prayer—whether a drop of rain was a single syllable. Whether if I re-lit the candle and drew back the curtain I would be able to see the oaks of any of the raindrops on the window, as if each one were a word, and as if oaks, or rockpools, were visible. As if oaks, or rockpools, could be lit by a pulse of distant lightning.

M

The following morning, my friend was gone. An ebullient note left on the kitchen table, with more than one triple-underline, told me how lovely it had been to see me, and insisted that we should not wait so long before the next time. I would forgive him, he said, for leaving without saying goodbye, in order to make a particular train, or to avoid a particularly long wait, I forget, and for helping himself to a frantic pot of coffee. He was right, but I noticed in my brittleness that he had used a lot of coffee. For a few seconds I stared across the room, at nothing in particular. My hangover had entered the nerve centre of my entire operation, and I was anxious about what it might do next.

There were a few oaks, actual oak trees, beautiful old oak trees, somewhere a few hundred yards beyond the wall I was staring at. It occurred to me what a strange pair of accidents it was that my friend had described to me these empty syllables, these gaps, pocks, caverns, and had named them in that spirit, yet I had stumbled into naming them after something so present, such a grand and exemplary instance of organic growth. I thought of their heaviness, their unambiguous presence, and could almost see them, as if I was staring through and beyond the wall—but I was staring through and beyond them too, unimaginable distances. Something or nothing shivered through me. I shook these confused thoughts out of my head, I folded the letter in half, I put it in my breast pocket, I turned on the tap, and I rinsed out the coffee pot. Later that day I wrote to my friend, to tell him about my hallucination, or maybe I called it a dream, or maybe I equivocated; and also to tell him about my discovery, that they were called oaks, for me. Perhaps anyone who has the dream will find their very own name for them, sooner or later: rockpools, or oaks, or whatever you find out they are called. Three more times I wrote, but I did not hear from or see my friend again.

69 Solar mill, again

It didn't happen, and I don't think I ever expected you to believe it did. That boyfriend did not exist, and I've never lived somewhere like that. A flat over two floors, in London, and neither of us wealthy? I do however claim it is true, in some sense. I did experience it. I woke up from it one morning, at the point where my telling stops.

Immediately on waking I knew that I wanted to retain the events of that imaginary day. I was having a breakdown, but was still two years away from realising that I was. What I was well aware of was that I had been totally isolated for just over a year. Fourteen months. I felt as if I needed those tendernesses not to vanish. I folded the four corners of a sheet of A4 paper near the bed, before going back to sleep again, because I had woken far too early. The folded corners were supposed to represent the four wobbling vanes inside the solar mill. It worked: later, I remembered.

It was not just that I wanted to hold on to the feeling of being in love, to the memory of all the small happy treats of the day. I wanted to write about them, or write with them. In the seconds after waking up, I was convinced that the dream was full of chains of symbols which made by chance a satisfying sense.

The details of that conviction slipped away quickly, too quickly for me to capture the symbols and chains and get them into sentences. And that symbol that wasn't a symbol, right at the dead centre of it, that delicate object breaking, precipitating the floods of tears we'd both been holding back: it felt like a too-obvious conceit, almost.

Lately I had been browsing my collected Cowper, and when I woke from this dream I found that I had in my head one of his winter walks, how that brittle day 'smiles.../ And has the warmth of May', as if it had been a key or a cheat-code to the whole thing which I hadn't been able to access from within.

Something which is true in a far more tangible way is that a few weeks before having that dream I had bought myself a solar radiometer. It arrived in early December, but I decided to leave it until the 25th to open it, a little gift for myself. In the aftermath of this dream, I was convinced that it was called a 'solar mill', a mangling of the two alternative names given in this real one's little leaflet: 'light mill' or 'solar engine'. To my beautiful dreamt boyfriend, I send my apologies (for quietly attributing that error to him). I do not know why I made the sudden decision to buy myself a solar radiometer, but I do know that for a few days in the run up to the dream I had been a little anxious about breaking it. This one isn't like the one I dreamed. It comes with a wooden base, into which a cylindrical protrusion of the glass bulb is supposed to fit. It doesn't go in as easily as you'd want.

When I was a boy, I remember there being a solar radiometer. Somewhere. One that was much more like the one in the dream: the base not an additional object but a flaring of the glass itself. For all that I now remember of it, I may as well have been absent for most of my childhood. But I am convinced there was a solar radiometer somewhere. Or a solar engine, or a light mill. I don't know if it was in my house, or in the house of a friend or a family member. I do remember being transfixed by it. It was an excellent thing in its own right, but it was also a cousin, somehow, of the cloud chamber.

The cloud chamber was something I had seen on television, and had immediately decided was one of the best things ever to exist. I was very into space, and rockets, and so on; and the Royal Institution Christmas Lectures by Frank Close had recently been inspiring enough that I sincerely wanted, at whatever age I was, to be a particle physicist when I grew up. Close had explained that the cloud chamber was devised a century or so ago, by a scientist who—I think this is how the story went—was keen to imitate in laboratory conditions the mists he so loved when out walking in Scotland. Close himself had seemed to be sincerely awed by it, thrilled to be in the presence of a functioning example.

This is thirty years ago, and my memory will provide no more detail than the following: the cloud chamber is a glass cabinet, to fit on a table, inside of which a radioactive *thing* is placed. Outwards from that thing, in all directions, silvery-grey trails fleck the air, and—just as gravity begins to act on them, as if they are the ghosts of fishing lines being slackened—they vanish.

The cloud chamber doesn't show you radiation itself, but it shows you the artefacts of its activity, of things coming briefly into contact with other things, the unseen jostling of tiny reality. Beautiful mist-like trails which are the evidence of interactions beyond our senses. Also in Close's lectures was set up a device which would ding a bell every time a particle radiated from a rock in the precise direction of a sensor somewhere. With the memory of all these devices, the images of particles and interactions swimming round my head, I convinced myself seconds after waking that the vanes of a solar radiometer spin because of little parcels of sunlight hitting them, turning them just as wind turns a windmill.

This is not what happens. I will be honest and say that when I woke up I felt sad and very lonely. I felt better, or at least distracted, while I was writing. Then, afterwards, I once again felt sad and very lonely.

In the dream, what had been my boyfriend's name? Details I was sure I'd known just seconds ago were no longer accessible to me. I found that I kept thinking of the phrase 'slipping away'. Lying in bed, wishing I could get back to that dreamt day, I wondered about inverting the image which gave rise to that phrase, 'slipping away'. What if dreams are not delicate, are not separated into fine grains upon waking, so that they might slip through fingers like sand, but are firm and intact structures, which become silted up by consciousness? Such that a dream becomes harder and harder to recall, the more awake we are, not because it disintegrates, but because it's becoming occluded by the noise of consciousness.

That kind of thinking to me is testament to how desperately I wished to go back to its world, to dream it again, to dream him again.

It is time to bring this chapter to a close, and I'm going to do that with a tiny anecdote. I'm remembering how, a few years ago, bored, I went online and posed a question. I claimed ('everyone knows') that if ever you wake up and find that suddenly you have grown one of those long, thin, silvery-grey eyebrow hairs, it means that the actor Geoffrey Bayldon has dreamt about you. However, Geoffrey Bayldon had recently passed on, at the grand age of ninety-three. With that in mind, I asked: Given that Geoffrey Bayldon is no longer with us, what must those eyebrow hairs mean now?

An answer from my friend D, almost instantly:

—That dreams don't die when you do.

70 A candle lit

Such a profoundly sad ghost in the room I woke in today. From fraught dreams which I think felt it too. As if all feeling greyed out, a subtle but thorough chill like the aftermath of an unheard chime in the air, and the wind whistling gently outside with a precise sound it hasn't had before, not for the whole time I've lived here. For a good few hours I felt and behaved like an anxious cat, not wanting to leave the room.

I opened the shutters, and a little more light got in, and as I stood there felt I close to tearful in a very physical way, as if there were actually a large vessel of liquid somewhere, unstable and threatening to overflow. I felt like it would be appropriate to close the shutters again; the room was not yet ready for the light, because something had happened here. That's how it felt. As a space it had also the sense of hosting, even of being, an end, or an ending. The process or processing of an end, or an ending. Something which, although I didn't understand it, I knew to be very precise, was soon going to be over.

Perhaps the sadness of the ghost, pressed into the room for however many hours, is beginning to diminish, but the impression left is of a habitat made inconsolable and raw—not unlike the brittleness of having been awake for far too long. In a strange way, I feel like I want to be there for it—for the ghost as much as for the room it haunted, which itself feels tender and undead. So I'm spending my afternoon in a small room, in very low light, feeling haunted. I may even light a candle.

That's a candle lit. The light is still utterly strange, around the shutters and the door, probably as even weak daylight, illuminating a space whose meaning for the time being is of an extraordinarily specific ending, seems incongruous and wrong. Whatever happened here this morning, the haunting seems to want the dark still. So I am sat here now, in a room where something happened, eating a small apple, hoping it doesn't mind, while I write about it—the way you sometimes trust that simply pottering around gently, in the presence of someone upset, may, in the absence of knowing how to help, offer a kind of humdrum solace. Company.

This is not fiction, by the way. This is a diary I'm writing about my day, as that day happens. I do not believe that ghosts are wholly fictional. I do believe that if they are in part constituted by fiction, then that makes them more beautiful, not less. Here is a paragraph I wrote one night, in the winter, beyond drunk, at a time when I had reason to think about ghosts a lot: I was living on K's boat.

> The only reason I believe in ghosts is I am alive. Ghosts are stories told by the living to the living:

I don't know what death is, but if I imagine what I am most scared of, it is not having access to the living, not having people to tell me stories, not having people to tell stories to. Someone dead has access to nothing. A ghost is a fiction created by someone living, a fiction that someone dead has access to the things of our world. Which they don't. The inevitable inverse of that idea is that someone living can have access to someone dead, and of course it's an idea which has been cynically, cruelly exploited. That particular fiction at its core implies that a consciousness which has access to nothing can not only imagine but manifest access to something. Which is another way of saying: that particular fiction collaterally invents a permanent hell. Access to nothing disguised as access to something.

The last bit I cannot fathom. It's very confused. At the time I was drinking vodka in such quantities that I'm surprised any of it makes sense. The bits that do, I'm not sure I agree with. My feeling about ghosts this afternoon—influenced I'm sure by the image I described earlier, tearfulness as somehow an encounter at the nudging, spilling tip of a vast holding of water—is that ghosts are themselves a little like tears. We often hear ghosts spoken of, whether in their vengefulness or their anger or their grief, as somehow immensely powerful. These supposed entities, whatever they may be, which in their vengefulness or their anger or their grief you must treat with a great deal of respect, because they are not to be fucked around with, not even in jest—such talk seems, I think, probably because it makes for good stories, to maintain a belief in ghosts as purposeful, and in hauntings as deliberate, and to manufacture and sustain a kind of excitable and curious wariness on our part. To keep us not necessarily fearful, but cautious. Another thing, though, which must be treated with a great deal of respect, especially in a context of sadness or anger or grief, is fragility, and vulnerability. The ghost that was here, in the room in which I woke this morning, did not, I am absolutely certain of this, mean to menace anyone. I am not at all sure that it was doing anything, or even existing anywhere, on purpose. My honest feeling is that it was here, for a short while, simply because it was so sad that it couldn't help it.

M

I've never forgotten how Thomas Henry Huxley, in an 1868 medical textbook, describes what happens as a result of (for instance) sadness:

> under certain circumstances, as when the conjunctiva is irritated by pungent vapours, or when painful emotions arise in the mind, the secretion of the lachrymal gland exceeds the drainage power of the lachrymal duct...

That fluid, 'at length overflows in the form of tears'. So that instead of thinking today of barriers between realities being broken, I am thinking of the presence of ghosts as more of an overflow of feeling, a temporary irruption of sadness, or anger, or grief, too great for the habitat of the dead to contain. Even 'irruption' is a word redolent of boundary-failure, or the breaching of membranes.

When the water of a natural spring emerges above ground, it does not do so violently, by puncturing anything, it simply travels; and what we observe is everything after that precise moment where the substance through which it is moving changes. I am suddenly remembering a field near where I used to live, in that particular middle of nowhere which is also the middle of Wales. The field used to flood, occasionally. It did that when there was more water than the ground could contain. They never used to let the cows into the field when it flooded, perhaps because cows have arrived at this image too—considering a quantity of water that will not drain away to be analogous to ghosts—and react immediately, in surprise or fear. An image of a field is perhaps more apt for ghosts than an image of tears overflowing from the eerie tunnels beneath your eyes.

Sometimes, when, somewhere, for something, some capacity is exceeded, we find ourselves sensing it, wondering whether a ghost is present. But as with tears—we do not call them that unless and until we cry them—we only name a ghost in the moment of its overflow, because only in such a haunting is it present to us. This morning's ghost seemed to be formed not from vengefulness, not from anger: it was only unspeakable sadness. So unspeakable that it exceeded the capacity even of death.

For now, I am still in the room where there was a ghost earlier. The room does feel a little less cold. This has been a precious and strange encounter, and I do not think cocooning in a small, darkened, harrowed room was a bad decision. I hope something, somewhere is recovering as it needs to.

71 Letter for Sean

26.11.2019, in memory of Sean Bonney

Chapter 10 begins:

> There is a type of social organisation characterized by a form of aggression that we have not yet encountered: the collective aggression of one community against another. I will try to show how the misfunctioning of this social form of intra-specific aggression constitutes 'evil' in the real sense of the word.

Those two sentences are from a book I'm reading. They're actually about rats; the chapter title is 'Rats'. Twinkle, twinkle. The only thing it is possible or okay to do right now is begin the task of gathering.

The five-hundred-thousandth rhyme for the word 'star' is a pattern of optimism shattering out of a layer of shifting clouds; it is all those bright edges. I think perhaps it is there in actual neon, I guess somehow we will find out. Behaviour among the smaller numbers is so irregular and the patterns though vivid so illusory that those brown and yellow leaves we noticed are in a different pile when somehow we loop past them again in freezing November drizzle, and a different pile again.

Recently in the dictionary I discovered that a braid formed from the idea of starlight and the idea of desire is still flickering at the glowing core of the word 'consider'—as if thinking is the desire to assemble stars, as if an idea is a constellation alighting suddenly in the absurd circumstance of a single human soul, is the sunlight shimmering off a shivering spider-web, is a poem, I mean, all of that—and for some reason I felt cold, like stony stairwells, like going outside for a cigarette. The speed of light is a nursery rhyme.

That's where this started. I had to try somehow to tell you about a conversation Sean and I once had about nursery rhymes: their perfection, their impossibility, their electrical storms of inscrutable human feeling, the immense history tumbling through a wooden frame which is things happening one after another in the rhythm of the playground—and when something rhymes it breaks through feeble concrete like a mushroom. It's nice I suppose that people associate spring with new growth, but it doesn't cover nearly enough. Before that conversation we had been crying so much together. After that conversation it was about 5 a.m. and for reasons best left to the ghosts we found a small pair of scissors and I gave Sean Bonney a haircut.

Ghosts, I knew they'd happen. I wanted to bring something for you, made of shoes and socks absolutely soaked by the damp ghosts of the climbing pavement.

It can be whatever kind of autumn it wants to be, pine cones, the weather, the canal, but it is edged by great queues of excitable ghosts, and it is extremely dangerous, and I am telling you now that it has every fucking right to be.

Let's say for the sake of getting through the day that all that is a nursery rhyme. Point in your hat and coat in the direction of: the lichen on the bark of slate-grey trees is a nursery rhyme. That the trees are the same colour as the city they are ornate skeletons of, that is a nursery rhyme, and the silverfish mice who scuttle across the tracks of the U-bahn teach it to their children, who are eloquent and hungry, and move like beads of rain on a bus window because they are eloquent and hungry. The seasons are a nursery rhyme, making a list is a nursery rhyme, traffic is a nursery rhyme, foxes are a nursery rhyme, I love you is a nursery rhyme, fuck the police is a nursery rhyme, this hurts is a nursery rhyme, and on top of all that: a pulse, any pulse, is a drumbeat, is an emergency, is a night and a day, and in the playground of collective speech a rhyme is an equinox is a social moment, is intensive care, is two identical vowels that lasso together all the plagues and monsters and gardens and sanctuaries of this immense chaotic nursery rhyme. And, it's a ghost. I don't know why we even have to remind people of that.

Half a pound of treacle sounds like a lot of treacle. There was a truly terrifying time when Sean and I stood staring out of his sixth-floor window as dawn happened, over Berlin. We avoided the balcony, because of a brief conversation on the topic of jumping from it, which, in the final analysis, Sean Bonney sagaciously advised me not to do. Don't do that, he said, as if someone had suggested putting diesel in a petrol engine without first making sure that the car belonged to the police. There had just been an election in America. We felt as if this was the end of everything. It was all ruined. A hot air balloon floated over Berlin every morning by the newspaper Die Welt refused to rotate so that we just stood there as it screamed at us the word 'DIE' in letters as big as the flat, which had at that moment no food in it.

I've been doing this for what, an hour and twenty minutes, and I've only just realised that it won't be the only one I do. It was stupid of me not to have known that from the start. It's a *mess*. What the fuck is going on, and I am sorry but why should any of us actually have to cope with this at all. Imagine the answer to that question. Imagine wearing it, like webbing, or chain mail, or anger. I forgot that earlier I thought it crucial to appeal to the image of a concrete shell extending across all that is knowable, blocking out the sun. Good. I was wrong.

> In their behaviour towards members of their own community the animals here to be described are models of social virtue; but they change into horrible brutes as soon as they encounter members of any other society of their own species.

That's from the same page of that book. For Tories, really actually do say rats. But never the other way around. I noticed while writing this letter that 'rats' is 'star' written backwards, but rats and stars can't help that. Fascists are the reverse of living and it's their own fucking fault.

Sometimes by the end of them the ghosts in his poems were whirling round so much it was like a wizard just calling forth the sea to do an entire castle of washing-up—and drowning the king, incidentally. But my favourite line by Sean for a while now has been:

> I love you all so fucking much.

There it is. That night, he said to me that next, what he wanted to write was nursery rhymes. And actually he made one up right away, only one. A joke that absolutely wasn't a joke. It was two lines about Frances.

In this timeline is there anything to say. It feels so facile, but, here goes—cutting a Tory's throat because it will bring out the best in you is 'pop goes the weasel'; 'for "I love you" say "fuck the police"' is 'up above the world so high': the playground injunction of the annihilation of these murderers is precisely the truth of injustice interacting with the overriding truth of a better universe, it is the truth of the cow jumping over the moon, it makes the exact same sense, and somewhere in language, there are schoolkids maintaining that truth. I hope we remain those schoolkids. We do not forget those rhymes.

There is a good bit in 'Twinkle, twinkle, little star'—if you stay up all night, re-angle the pronouns, make an equinox of it, and let it breathe, so that it reflects the early morning light a little differently, it goes 'how we wonder / what we are'.

72 Late-evening daydream of the Pequod

breathe

breathe

breathes

breathing

breath

breathing

breath

breaths

breaths

breaths

breaths

breathing

breath

breathe

breathes

breathes

breath

breath

In a dark room sit at a desk, ready in this case to open Moby-Dick. But not yet. In a moment. You cannot see a thing yet, not the book, not even your own hands. This daydream is about a whaling ship; your unlit room might well be on a ship too. First fumble for the matchbox, it gently rattles, light the candle. Now see the desk, the book, the matches, a tin, an ashtray, an empty glass—and for our purposes notice also that there is a small mirror. Circular, to fit in a palm. It is extremely cold in the room. Your own breath in the light of the flame becomes visible, a silver dance lit gold of melting rondels in the frozen air. Yes, it is pleasing to see it, but the obvious question: what about a more directed breath, a more forceful plume of vapours?

So you inhale: and you shape with your mouth that aperture which sharpens an exhalation into a jet, the air in your mouth a ready missile. Only don't yet exhale [Fig. 1]. Hold for the briefest pause to notice your mouth. And don't point it straight at the candle! Make sure you won't extinguish it: you'll need that light to read by, in a moment, and of course to see your jet of breath. Now, exhale. A jet or spout or spurt or geyser of visible breath. A grand fountain of vapour.

Is there something on the surface of the mirror? Bring it closer. Inhale: prepare to steam it up with a loose, mouth-open delivery of wide mist, as if deep in your chest a vast piston is primed. Only don't yet exhale [Fig. 2]. Hold for the briefest pause to notice your mouth. Now exhale. And the mist of droplets on the mirror makes of it an unreflecting disc of cloud.

On the desk in the tin is a small amount of tobacco, if you want it. That crack'd archangel Captain Ahab suddenly quits smoking in Chapter 30, flings his pipe into the sea, but second-mate Stubb is smoking absolutely all the time. Says Ishmael, 'You would almost as soon have expected him to turn out of his bunk without his nose as without his pipe.' Figures 1 and 2 are not printed here, they are not illustrations to accompany instructions; they are temporary names for the shapes of your mouth in the two given contexts. Fig. 1 plus an exhalation might also be called blowing; or if a pitch is heard, whistling. An exhalation via Fig. 2 might be called a sigh. If you first have in your lungs (for instance) tobacco smoke, the visible results of exhaling after 1 or 2 respectively are almost the same as with breath in a cold room: the one a directed jet, the other a grand chaotic waft. A fine-tuned combination of the two is said to be the secret behind smoke rings.

In English, figures 1 and 2 are close enough to the preparations for consonants we have letters for: an unvoiced 'w' and a pure 'h'. Some speakers begin 'wh' words as if the figures are reversed ('hw'), that first sigh tightened up into a whistle, or rather into a blow. This consonant to blow out a candle is called a *voiceless labial-velar fricative*. It has a symbol:

ʍ

Open the book. Herman Melville, whether he wants to or not, draws attention to these letters, these two figurations (of the mouth)—and to the engine (the lungs) behind their fountains and spouts—immediately. Long before the action of *Moby-Dick* begins, before Ishmael's infamous introduction, before even the page-upon-page of quotations about whales and whaling ('EXTRACTS'), you will find the very first text of the book itself, on the leaf after the dedication to Hawthorne. It is a tiny chapter titled 'ETYMOLOGY', which offers a brief study of the word 'whale', as if that is the embryo of the book, the primordial structure, the first cell to divide. It begins with everything in parentheses: first they are rounded, then they are squared at the corners. This 'ETYMOLOGY', says its subtitle, was '(Supplied by a Late Consumptive Usher to a Grammar School.)' Then someone remembers that Usher:

> [The pale Usher—threadbare in coat, heart, body, and brain...]

This reminiscence done with, we are on with the business of the day. Of those languages whose whale-words appear in the list supplied, most begin with either an 'h' or a 'w', or some combination of the two:

WHŒL,	Anglo-Saxon.
HVALT,	Danish.
WAL,	Dutch.
HWAL,	Swedish.
HVALUR,	Icelandic.
WHALE,	English.

It is perhaps a shame that Melville (or his Usher) gets 'WHŒL' wrong; indeed some editions give 'WHÆL', a little closer. Anglo-Saxon for 'whale' was 'hwael', just a single cross-trees on the mast of the 'l' away from being 'hwaet'. The Anglo-Saxon name of the creature behind Melville's own epic, the atom at its origin, is a stroke away from that shout, to alert an audience and grab their attention, with which the Beowulf poet opened theirs. What a harpoon of a word. And what a frivolous observation to make. I hope Melville wouldn't mind.

Anyway: just before this list, he quotes the colonialist author Richard Hackluyt, on a very grave error indeed:

> While you take in hand to school others, and to teach them by what name a whale-fish is to be called in our tongue, leaving out, through ignorance, the letter H, which almost alone maketh up the signification of the word, you deliver that which is not true.

So, by this daydream's logic, doesn't Hackluyt's claim seem to be as follows: of all the letters in the word, the one freighted with most meaning is the silent sigh?

Behind exhalations, before mouths tautened to a whistle, behind and before everything here, are lungs. The vital, motivating mystery is pulmonary—which brings us back to this Usher, the very first character in all of *Moby-Dick*. We only meet him briefly. The earliest two shreds of information are: firstly, he is dead, and secondly, he has chewed-up lungs. He had pulmonary tuberculosis, and probably died of it. This poor Usher's first adjectives, 'late' and 'consumptive', are a sinister and specific inversion of the familiar pair 'living' and 'breathing'; and the only paragraph dedicated to this unfortunate man shifts from the present tense of memory ('I see him now') to a past-tense narrative immediately, and ends by reminding us, via this Late Consumptive Usher's past ponderings, as he dusted his grammars, of 'his own mortality.'

We were already minded very much of his mortality: he stopped breathing, he is dead. As our narrator remarks, a great deal later:

> ...whatever other business [man] has to attend to, waking or sleeping, breathe he must, or die he will.

That's from Chapter 85, 'The Fountain'. If the early Usher's presence is the faint odour of a latent fascination with breathing, with lungs, and if that fascination is a quietly present mycelium throughout *Moby-Dick*, then it fruits extravagantly in Chapter 85, when our narrator comes to muse upon that wonder of the natural world which is the whale's spout, or fountain.

M

An aside: of all the chapters in this vast book, 85 is the only one given a time-stamp—and parenthetically so, as if through some aperture in (or into) the text appears a glimpse of the reality of its composition:

> this blessed minute (fifteen and a quarter minutes past one o'clock P.M. of this sixteenth day of December, A.D. 1850)

Is that a wild claim? That this precision-dating comes from, is a brief index of, the living, breathing Melville? So what if it is. By the way, the first American edition gave this date as 1851, which was the year of publication. Melville corrected the error for the English edition, but it has occasionally persisted. A Penguin Classics *Moby-Dick* has 1850, but a Penguin

Popular Classics *Moby-Dick* has 1851, as if the digit is a tally of the word 'Popular' in the imprint. You could use them to count, in binary. I have too many copies of this book: the largest number I can make with them is 32752. Where was it, this daydream?

M

It is still a problem, says our narrator, 'whether these spoutings are, after all, really water, or nothing but vapor.' When a whale exhales through its blowhole, what was vapour condenses; and in such quantities, a great deal is blown out as water. Ahab sees this transubstantiation a little differently when later he kills a whale:

> All thy unnamable imminglings float beneath me here; I am buoyed by breaths of once living things, exhaled as air, but water now.

But the whale's spouting definitely is an exhalation, one which becomes water or vapour again; or, so as not to make it sound like a sigh, perhaps it is more of a jet, a directed exhalation, almost a whistle, as if its blowhole is lined with mirrors.

The lungs behind this huge exhalation are fascinating for Ishmael, or for Melville, and the superordinating fact of Leviathanical breathing is felt in just how often we encounter the words 'breath' or 'breathes' (etc.) in this chapter. More than a third of their occurrences in the entire book are found in this miniature rhapsody. (The cloud of breath-words at the start here is a table of these words, in the order they appear in Chapter 85.)

But that pipe, poor whale, was thy last.

That same whale, which saw Ahab transforming in his imagination air to water, is afforded by Ishmael the luxury of the metaphor of smoking, for his spoutings. The whale is even, almost, given a miniature funeral, when in a strange and not-quite-tender moment Stubb remarks that both its pipes are out, then scatters the ashes from his own pipe into the sea.

Take a look at your cigarette. Tobacco in *Moby-Dick* is its own pattern, has many things to tell us. Stubb's good nature is directly attributed (by Ishmael) to his pipe-smoking. Queequeg's tomahawk, a formidable weapon at one end, is at the other end a pipe: it is the opposite of war, it is a symbol of Queequeg at his most companionable; and indeed a smoke together marks some of the most intimate moments between him and his bosom friend. Perhaps this list, from Chapter 85 again, reminds us as much of smoke as of steam:

> I am convinced that from the heads of all ponderous profound beings, such as Plato, Pyrrho, the Devil, Jupiter, Dante, and so on, there always goes up a certain semi-visible steam, while in the act of thinking deep thoughts.

And, of course, there is Ahab—in the miracle which is Chapter 30, 'The Pipe':

> How now. This smoking no longer soothes.

We have barely met Ahab when he gives up his pipe. Long before this, smoking has already come to denote affability, sociability, a sound and serene mind—and Ahab jettisons his tobacco, musing that it no longer soothes him, immediately before disclosing his maniacal mission to the crew, on 'The Quarter-Deck' (so Chapter 36 is titled) of the Pequod. But here, in this moment, to himself, alone:

> Here have I been unconsciously toiling, not pleasuring—aye, and ignorantly smoking to windward all the while; to windward, and with such nervous whiffs, as if, like the dying whale, my final jets were the strongest and fullest of trouble. What business have I with this pipe?

Captain Ahab deranges in his mind these plumes, or fountains; he considers his own tobacco smoke and mingles it with the vastest exhalation of the maritime cosmos. He flings his pipe into the sea; and as its lit parts dampen, the Pequod sails past, and leaves it, along with Ahab's sanity, to the ocean.

ʍ

This daydream is smoke and mirrors—and candle-light and vapours—and although perhaps its core image is Ahab throwing his pipe in the sea, it began with a tiny moment. As the book begins with a focus on the word 'whale', at its very start, this daydream's spark was the shape of the mouth at the very start of that word—ready to exhale tobacco smoke, or to blow a candle out so as to return a small room to darkness.

Every now and again in reality a substance is forced out from its containment through an aperture into a void. In this daydream, air or smoke; and the void may be a room, or may be the great open ocean rolling, the sound of gulls above. Air from our lungs, air from a whale's lungs. Tobacco smoke from Stubb's, from Ahab's, from yours or mine. The symbols or sigils 'h' and 'w', or those combinations, 'wh' or 'hw', may be assigned to certain of these manoeuvres, if the aperture in question is a mouth.

What consonant Ahab produced, in the very last of his quick and constant puffs, before quitting his pipe forever, is not beyond all conjecture. The ghost of which consonant does a whale sound, when it exhales through a blowhole—this puzzling question I leave to the deep and tormented dark.

Your cigarette has nearly gone out, your tobacco has run out. So, leaning closer to the flame, ready at last to extinguish it, inhale, air or smoke, your choice: and shape with your mouth that aperture which sharpens an exhalation into a jet [Fig. 1]. *Breath held, staring right at the flame. Only, don't yet exhale—*

DERELICT

73 The windfarm

Look out at the channel, from Brighton. The windfarm is eerie when none of the rotors are turning, and very beautiful. Deathly still, filament-thin vertical rods. It was even more uncanny earlier this evening when the sea and the sky were indistinguishable in colour, and there was haze enough that the horizontal line usually separating them was invisible, which I suppose in the case of this horizontal line in particular is the same as saying you couldn't see the horizon. The windfarm was still visible, but indistinct in the mist. It looked like a run of silk stitches over a near-healed wound, such that they were beginning to melt away, and looked even as if they might soon drop off. When the horizon is invisible I always feel a little overwhelmed to look at where it ought to be; sea and sky together become so enveloping and oppressive, a perfect and impervious and textureless membrane—no wonder that anything in front of them comes to look fragile, and only provisionally anchored, a foreign body at the very end of an invisible or at least unseen process of ejection.

It's dark now and the windfarm is invisible, except for the fact that—precisely because of its night-time invisibility—each of the vast pillars is fitted with a red light, making for a colonnade of them, all at the exact same height, which blink 'W' in Morse code from twilight through til dawn. Dot-dash-dash. Sometimes, my brain ignores the meaning of the code and simply adds words to the rhythm. It's a mystery to me where they come from. The darkened windfarm tonight by the skin of its teeth is transmitting the blinked-out bulletin:

I'm still here

I'm still here

I'm still here

I'm still here

74 Markers, buoys

19.10.2020—Something happened to me today. It was as if grief revealed itself unbidden to exist in a few more dimensions than I had previously felt, or rotated around some new axis. Its shape seems changed, new symmetries have been revealed. Its beauty is new and different.

I'm barely coping. Lockdowns, tiers, the pandemic in general, the murderous ghouls in government, my own terrible mental health, and being forcibly uprooted from the city I'd called home for ten years. I keep finding myself envisaging days, weeks, months, as simply a vast wall of ice on which I am somehow climbing. I can't see more than a few yards up or down or left or right because of the fog: where the fuck am I, and where do I go? I imagine meaningful days, significant moments on which to hang preparation, planning, orientations, as struts, or pickaxes, stuck out from the ice, visual anchors: and when they are entirely absent, as they tend to be, I imagine fixing them there myself, jamming things violently into the ice, or failing to. If there is nothing to be meaningful then I must create meaning artificially. Even a to-do list feels like handholds or footholds in the ice.

Out of all of this what today came to rescue me was sadness. It has somehow righted me, gifted me with a day of stability and orientation. It's been a day to make me very aware that sadness is not the same thing as depression. This sadness feels healthy, like being alive. I absolutely ought to be sad.

Two years ago I would have been in too much pain to imagine ever describing grief as beautiful. I would have been furious at the very idea, and probably spiteful and unpleasant about it. Today, something seemed to be happening to me, and I decided to embrace it, to write along with it. It felt as if what I must do is sit with the grief, acknowledge it for what it is, and let it river through my day—and through my soul, if you like—let it behave just as it wants to. For a long time I have wanted to write something for somebody, in his memory. This isn't that. This is just a brief note about him, something which I had not today expected to be writing, and I'm doing it because today is my birthday.

M

K was my best friend. People sometimes have a problem with that phrase, but I never thought of him as anything else, and never will; and it still feels like I may never use the phrase about anyone again. We were incredibly close. We met in the winter of 2014, and after just a couple of months we were doing life together. Not all of it, but a great deal of it. The second time I met his mother was a few days after he had died, and at one point, she said to me: 'He said it was as if you'd known each other forever.' At which I expect I cried. That is precisely how I felt about him, though I had not until that moment thought of expressing it that way.

Sometimes people thought we were a couple, which was fair enough. We did love each other and we said so. We saw each other every day; we did almost everything together. He was almost exactly twenty years older than me, but he was one of those ageless people, and birdlike, with it. Just as plausibly a tiny gangly sparrow as an ancient, cantankerous owl, often both in the same moment.

He was with me in the pub four years ago, in October 2016; we were having a cigarette outside when it ticked over to midnight of the 19th, and he insisted on taking a photo for immediate upload, captioned 'this boy is now 30'. One year later we were, quite rudely, almost an hour late to my own birthday gathering in The Foundry. He had got me dinner in a new Greek place on London Road. That was the last time I ever saw him.

Two and a half years of grief ebbing and manifesting and wrenching and abating, and I woke up today once again under its shadow, but that shadow was not baleful or overwhelming this time. This has not been a bad day. It is not the shadow of a ghoul or a tyrant or a black dog, nor even of a heartbreak. It is more like, somehow, the shadow of the healing of a heartbreak; it felt like a kindly darkening across all similar days in my future, tincturing them with the sense of an evening, an autumn, an ending. I can feel it casting this shadow over a good deal of my future birthdays, and I welcome that, I am finding solace in it. It is a strange and indifferent accident that the last time I got to see the man I loved was my birthday; but I've never liked doing anything on my birthday, so what better way to spend these awkward yearly recurrences than remembering him.

K's birthday, by the way, was on Boxing Day. He never liked that; it was always overshadowed by the general chaos of the time of year. But on his 49th, a large gathering was arranged in the Great Eastern, and he had the very best time. A big birthday party, at last! So a few of us named the 26th of December after him. As a consequence the 25th, which is traditionally a busy day for its own reasons, gained an alternative name, to reflect its being the eve of K's birthday.

M

At his funeral, K's mother read excerpts from a diary he had been keeping. Out of all of it, I remember only this:

'I'm going to fucking get better.'

—because I heard S. start crying behind me.

It was toward the autumn of 2017 when K began suffering from akathisia, a hellish side effect from prescription anti-depressants. By the winter he had gone to live with his mother, because he was no longer able to look after himself on his small, cluttered boat, moored in Brighton marina. After just four months of these side-effects, although he never wanted to die, he could not cope with the suffering of being alive any more, so he took himself back to Brighton, or back to Sussex at least, and he went into the woods and he curled up to sleep having made certain preparations. It was a beautiful, bright morning, and for most of the day nobody knew that he had killed himself.

In his diaries he had written that we should not think of what he had chosen to do as a suicide. More along the lines of euthanasia. He wanted to live—he said so repeatedly, and his diary bore that out—but by the time winter was turning to spring he no longer could.

M

Sometimes it feels as if dates—which ought really to retain some sense of their own arbitrariness, at least without our intervention—unexpectedly do the work themselves of becoming meaningful; of becoming somehow less inert, not just briefly proud of the surface of the calendar only to melt back into it but yoked to each other; of becoming more connected than merely flecks in a duration. Of becoming dyads, sutures, filaments.

Here's something I wrote about Wednesday June 4, 2015. I put it online a few days after K died.

> A few years ago I had to abandon a psychiatric assessment a few minutes in because on the way there my boyfriend had bullied me so badly that I couldn't talk to them, I couldn't stop crying. It was K who I met for coffee after that happened, because I needed rescuing, and he did it so well that we found ourselves in the blazing summer sun bounding around central Brighton in slow motion like it was unbelievable, and talking about having wound up in Brighton, and about having finally found a group of people we could belong with—we spoke about that a lot—and talking about how impossibly magic everything could be sometimes. It is quite simply my happiest memory, ever: holding hands with K, walking slowly north along Gardner St, talking about how happy we were. It was the opposite of today, it was sunny and it was almost too hot and I was sober and K was happy and alive. And carrying a friend's accordion in a box, I think. We definitely sat on the benches outside The Heart And Hand, which is a very important place to sit.
>
> A few hours later, about forty people turned up at my house because KN and K and I had put on an evening of music, poetry, anything, inviting

people to perform things either by J.S. Bach or Ivor Cutler. Which explains the accordion. There must have been twenty performances. This was the first one after K had agreed to MC these things, because I was too anxious, and he was brilliant at it. He just gently held the room, and I think a few of us acknowledged for the first time, because we could see it, that we remembered he'd been a schoolteacher. He sort of wrapped things up by wondering aloud why this weird juxtaposition had worked so well, and talked about his belief that Bach and Cutler may have been impossibly distant and different but at their core had a common kindness. He didn't say anything forceful or try to tie up any threads, just wondered aloud.

For much of 2016 and 2017 K and I were depressed, and talked often about how some kinds of magic and happiness were perhaps permanently inaccessible to us now, and were broken, stuck in the past. We said 'nothing works' a lot, quoting the great philosopher Catweazle. But that day the previous summer had been such a bright instance of when everything worked, one where things lined up and locked together and people were happy. Happiest day of my life, maybe. Among the best. He's gone. It's bullshit.

On the afternoon of June 4, 2018, six of us gathered to scatter his ashes. So for me those two June 4ths, three years apart, cannot but invite themselves to be roped together as kindred markers, buoys floating on the surface of his story, which has been so much my story too, and so much so many other people's.

When I began writing this, markers in time were violent juttings from a cliff of ice. Now they are buoys on a sea-surface. I don't feel an image of shadows lengthening across beautiful evenings could ever be autochthonous to so inhospitable a world as a sheer wall of ice, the visibility wretched for fog. Above the changeability of a sea-surface, gorgeous sunsets can hover. They do, notoriously. Besides, K had everything to do with the sea. He lived in a boat! And he had plenty of theories about the moon, which eases itself into every evening, beautiful or otherwise, and shatters itself into images of itself through any given sea.

'It sings', said K, more than once, 'and that harms people. But not deliberately.'

75 Ruined choirs

When first I became haunted it was deep within a dream, the fifth or even the seventh narrative inward. The haunting affected everyone. I was at a funeral, but I don't know whose funeral. The church was in fenland. It had sunk about two feet into the ground so we'd all had to almost climb in. The evening sky was deep orange, and there were two huge trees in the far distance, pitch-black and dense against the glow. I recall an absolute conviction that these trees were becoming sacred, as we stared at them.

The haunting was toward the end of the funeral. We were all singing a beautiful, solemn hymn, one based on an old French troubadour melody. It was in D minor. Just before the final verse, we all sang two lines that were not in the hymn book, to a melody which was not printed there. There was a tense pause before the congregation began to look at each other, wondering what had happened, and how. It would have been a silence except that the anxious organist, not knowing how to proceed, held a single thin note. The words had come from nowhere, and so had the melody they were sung to.

Nobody spoke, but everybody looked concerned, as well as lost, as if they had forgotten something significant and familiar. Startled as I was to have sung these lines, I felt just as startled that I could not summon the next two. We had sung, together:

> Darker in the light than in the half-light,
> Lighter in the dark than in the mid-day sun

It seemed obvious that there should be some answering phrase, some completion of the quatrain. It was not simply that no more text came to us. It truly felt like we had all known it, and had all forgotten it. The absence of those next lines was a pressing presence. The single sustained note from the organ was still the only sound.

When I awoke, the light told me it was almost dusk. I creaked myself upright, stressed and sweaty. I resent waking late, let alone this late. Waking up after hours upon hours of excess sleep only superficially resembles waking up proper, I think. My mind feels clogged, and its sunken windows on the world may as well be at the bottom of a swimming pool somewhere. I put on the pyjama trousers which, really, I should have been wearing already, given the heating isn't going on this winter, and loped with a hostile air to the bathroom. Already I was on some level finding my bad temper ever so slightly funny, but I was committed to it, and I obstinately refused to allow the self-awareness to surface.

It was dingy on the landing, and it was dingy in the bathroom. Grey and miserable, as if everything had been too much diluted. The bathroom light, when

I pulled the cord and the loud click echoed, made absolutely no difference. It felt very much like a washed-out Sunday afternoon, which is what it was. I turned the light off again, then on again, then off again, then on again—and I was going to turn it off again, only I had noticed a dissonance. The buzzing of the circuits I had last year in a moment of boredom tested against a keyboard. F, two Fs above middle C. Now the buzzing was clashing with another note, the E a semitone below. It was as if I was in the presence of two mosquitoes. I turned the light off, and listened to what remained, to the single sustained E. It wasn't from the room; it was in my own ears. How long had this tinnitus been there, I wondered. And I realised: since the anxious organist had pressed the key.

Shoving the heels of my hands hard into my closed eyes I tried to concentrate on the sound, to see if I could get rid of it. I could not. I half expected to be able to see the dreamt church again, to hear the cracking of the elderly pews and the rustle of clothing. Nothing. Nothing but the single thin note, that high E, as present as glass being looked through.

I went for a piss and washed my hands and cleaned my teeth and splashed cold water over my face. The towel, which was very cold, felt wet. I padded to my bedroom, prepared to cast a stupid, accusatory look at my alarm clock, a curse for its having dared to let me sleep til dusk like this. From the cabinet by the bed, where should have been my cheap plastic alarm clock, a starling launched itself at me.

I swore. I knocked stuff over trying to get out of its way. It was furious. I was ready to simply get out of the room and slam the door, but it flew to another corner. It was bigger than I expected a starling to be. My dreams were vanishing from my memory, but even in the chaos of having a panicked bird shitting all over my bedroom, I felt straight away that this event, of everything I'd encountered in the last few hours, ought not to be counted among the real ones. Yet here it was, forcing me to confront it as real, fortifying itself on a pile of my things, and behaving like it would tear my face off if I got too close.

Then I realised. I could not hear it. It was screeching at me, visibly, in fear and distress and with phenomenal aggression, but I heard nothing other than this high E, held on a single manual of an unreal church organ. Returning to my first idea, I backed off, in the direction of the bedroom door. My alarm clock was on the floor, presumably knocked by the bird, so I grabbed it and quit the room abruptly.

Instinctively I wanted to check that the alarm was working, so I went to switch it to 'on' and to move the alarm-trigger hand to the current time. But it was wrong, like a dream object. Everything seemed to be wrong. It was already set to 'on'. Looking at the hands I saw that it was still morning. My alarm had not gone off because it was not due to go off for another hour and a quarter. I screwed up my face and shook my head, the way I would have shaken the alarm clock—frustration at it, for its apparent refusal to work correctly, simultaneous with a crude attempt to rattle and jolt it back to normal behaviour. From the radiator in the bathroom I grabbed a towel.

The plan was to throw the towel at the bird. The plan did not yet have a next step. Perhaps the bird would remain still enough that I could carefully wrap the towel around it and then take the bird outside. Or throw it out of a window. With that thought, I realised I had no idea how it had got in. I pushed the bedroom door open. For a few seconds I stared at it as it yammered at me to stay back, increasingly disturbed that it made no sound. This emissary from chaos, beautiful as it was, which had bolted without warning into my life, was screaming at me, but I could not hear it.

Outside, a lorry roared past. It startled me such that I gasped. And as I gasped, I realised that in the roar of the lorry I had heard the screaming bird. Now it was silent again. I found that I froze. I simply stood there, poised to pounce with my towel in my hands, but not moving. I was fixed looking at the starling, waiting for the noise of traffic again, so that I could hear it again, all its alarm and threat.

I imagined walking along a dark street, well past midnight, holding this screaming starling in my hands, passing through the darkness between the glow of one streetlamp and the next, passing through the orange glow, passing through the darkness between that lamp and the next, on and on, with its screaming getting louder and louder the more light we were in, and fading to silence as we went further into the dark.

I imagined walking along a dark street, well past midnight, holding this screaming starling in my hands, passing through the darkness between the glow of one streetlamp and the next, passing through the orange glow, passing through the darkness between that and the next, on and on, with its screaming getting quieter and quieter the more light we were in, until fully silent under the direct glow of a lamp. I imagined the street running out, the regular lighting coming to an end, and the starling's muted shrieking increasing to an unbearable shrillness as I carried it on into total darkness.

It escaped. I had only made it a few steps beyond the front door when the starling, I suppose realizing we were outside, wrestled its way out of the towel and flapped itself to the ground. I watched it for a few seconds. It seemed much happier. Suddenly I yawned. When I opened my eyes, the starling was gone. A bus roared past, hissing as it did. Inside the roar and hiss I did not hear the starling. Back inside, I put some clothes on.

The skate park in the corner of the park was empty. The whole park was empty. I became aware that something about the environment was making me feel desperately upset. I felt like I was at work. I felt like I was stuck in an airport. It was as if there were no shadows; everything felt flat, grey, almost seemed to glow with flatness and greyness, under a menacing canopy of orange.

The light was what people want to call 'apocalyptic'. Everything was the same; no object could be distinguished from any other object, just as no thought or feeling could be differentiated from any other thought or feeling. Reality seemed moulded from a flavourless, slightly greasy liquid.

After standing in the same place for several hours, wondering if perhaps I was unwell, I heard the click of the floodlight lamp above the skate park. It had absolutely no effect on the dilute grey, the pale orange, the loss of every object's identity. Ordinarily, I was unable to look at the floodlight, and would have a dazzle of aftervision for a few seconds. Now, I stared right at it, and it did nothing to anything. I looked up at the silhouettes of some trees against the sky and felt sure that as I watched them they were becoming meaningless, indistinct, were being allowed to drain away by some immense cosmic indifference. The pressing presence of the coming absence made manifest in yellow leaves, or none, or few.

And the absence of birdsong. At length I felt tearful, as if I was a haunting made of absolute loss. I had a memory of the meaning of distinctions like summer and winter, but it was hurtful to look around me and find no such differences. Everything existed as if a banal average had been taken. I had absolutely no idea what time it was. I felt closer to the note I heard, sustained on that dreamt organ, than to any of the trees or buildings I could see. Perhaps it was time to sleep. I curled up where I was, and shut my eyes.

76 To the left of the origin

19.10.2022—As I write this I am looking at a strange little artefact. I've had it for just over twenty years. It is nearest to me, physically, so perhaps it is where I will start.

Bath Place is a narrow passage in Taunton, edged by small shops. One biting winter's day, I was walking down it. I was fifteen or sixteen. Outside the small paved area in front of the bookshop there was on this day a potter, stood behind a stall of his wares. I had never seen him before, and I never saw him again after this. He must have been six and a half foot tall, and large, padded gorgeously and cosily in layers upon layers of clothing, the outermost of which was a chaotic patchwork of fleece and suede in deep purples and browns; and his face and neck were likewise protected from the biting cold with a magnificent orange-grey beard. He gave the impression that he belonged as much to the woods as to our society: he was both a tree and a man, both a grizzly bear and a wizard. He looked like he had wandered out of a Maurice Sendak drawing to bring wisdom and good humour to this dark corner of Taunton town centre on a bitterly cold day.

I looked through the objects on this potter's cart. One of them caught my eye: it was a tiny bowl, or saucer, maybe five centimetres across. It looked misshapen; its scalloped edges were uneven; it had a sun-like spiral design in the centre, and the turquoise glaze with brown flecks was lopsided, like a cloud front on a weather map. The underside was completely unglazed. This wrong little object had a price tag which said '-1P'. I don't remember whether I picked it up, and I don't remember what I asked him, but I must have asked the potter something, because he said:

—Some things make their own way into the world. Others need a little help.

He would, he explained, give me a penny to take this object home with me. I think he knew, immediately, from my grin, that I wanted to take this off his hands and give it a home. Twenty years later, I still have it, and the price tag is still on it. It did go missing though, and for some time.

M

Four or five years later, again in the middle of winter—in the very deepest and darkest stretch of December—I was drinking in a South London pub, where my friend M was working. I waited for him to finish his shift. We were long overdue for a catch-up, and on the way back to his place in the Brandon Estate we bought some cans, a bottle of whisky, and a bottle of ginger wine.

We drank into the small hours, not chaotically but with commitment. We consumed a lot of alcohol, fortifying ourselves against the cold. We drank and smoked and talked for hours, never really noticing just how drunk we had got. At one point, during the witching hour, or perhaps even after it had passed, he taught me a song. This is how it begins:

They took us jolly sailor lads
A-fishing for the whale.
On the first day of August in 1864
Bound for Greenland we set sail.

This is 'The Greenland Whale Fisheries', of which there are so many versions. You may recognize the version he taught me as that sung by The Watersons. They do it in simple two-part harmony, and within the hour, once I had learned the words and the tune, M sang that harmony part. It was a wonderful thing to be doing, at the coldest, darkest time of year. There is nothing quite like it, singing with other people. (I remember that Kafka is enthusiastic on this point, with a startlingly violent image: singing with other people, he says, is like being caught in the cheek with a fish-hook. I think that's somewhere in *Meditation*.)

It was years before I in turn taught 'The Greenland Whale Fisheries' to someone else. By then, I'd been living in Brighton for five years. My friend E had been talking about singing together for a while. One night, we got round to it, and I taught her this song, just as M had taught it to me. For whatever reason, '1864' became a point of difficulty, and we decided to change the year to the mistake we most often made. As far as we were concerned, the jolly sailor lads set sail in 1869.

At the time, I lived a shared house with a very large living room. Large enough not just to fit an upright piano in, but even to function as a venue: in that room, in collaboration with friends, I put on evenings of music, poetry, of performance generally; twenty or thirty of them over the years. I've mentioned one of the best, Cutler/Bach, already. Such a thing seems impossible in Brighton now: a big room, in someone's house, big enough for socializing, big enough for rehearsals and even for gigs, which hadn't yet been carved up into multiple separate bedrooms, each going for an insane monthly rent.

That room could also be somewhere to rehearse if a small group of singers wanted to make a lot of noise. Which, starting in autumn 2015, is exactly what we did. Initially, it was just the two of us who met to sing; but soon it was three, then four or five. Some people came along just the once; some people came along and then never missed an evening. We met every Tuesday, starting and ending in the pub, and sang folk songs together. We sang, always, unaccompanied. Most of us did not read music, or know theory, but one of us was in a performing folk band. Working with singers and choirs happened to be one of my actual jobs at the time, and my training and experience was sometimes useful, but on the whole the two circumstances were entirely different. It was beautiful chaos, always.

'The Greenland Whale Fisheries' was the first song we did. Half of us learnt the harmony line. Next, we were taught the 'Mingulay Boat Song', a gorgeous fake 'Scottish folk-song' written by an Englishman in the 1930s; and we were taught, as winter approached, a cheerful version of 'The Holly And The Ivy' which none of us had ever heard before, a lilting 6/8 melody.

Over the next two or three years, these gatherings became very important to us. Singing—as everything got harder, and all our lives relentlessly got that little bit more pinched and cruel—brought us together, and it held us. Privately, it was nourishing and healing. Publically, we started to perform. We even got given a name. We turned up at someone else's flat one night, singing the 'Mingulay Boat Song' at his door, while he led something called Drawing Club. He was giving up an evening a week to teach his friends life drawing. Our gang got given the name 'Singing Club', simply because we 'invaded' Drawing Club that night.

It was an extraordinary year for these 'clubs': friendship circles in Brighton widened and intersected magically, with all these impromptu meetings and societies springing up regularly, in which people shared skills, taught each other things, and played music together. There was another, which I always wanted to get to but never did, called Mbira Club. Our friend R, who had been taught to play mbira, sourced a small arsenal of spares, and every week taught their friends to play them, and taught everyone the songs that went with the music. Sincerely, those were some of the most beautiful live performances I have ever attended.

Our friend M (another M) once put on a night, in a venue above a pub in town: on the bill were her band, another friend's band, and Mbira Club, and Singing Club. The flyer said: 'Drawing Club will be drawing Singing Club.' Drawing Club sat at the front, and they drew us while we sang. M afterward was in a bit of trouble with the venue: they'd lost money, they said, because 'everyone in the audience was a fucking performer' and so had earned themselves free entry and a free drink. That's what 2015 in Brighton felt like, though; and some of that spontaneously communistic energy carried us well into 2016. Only some of it, though. Things did begin to fall apart.

M

Today is my birthday. Five years ago, on my thirty-first birthday, was the last time I ever saw K. Five years on, I don't miss him every day. Somehow, that has happened. Two years ago, I still did; and I spent that birthday wracked with grief. I was surprised at how torrentially upset I was, from the very moment I woke up, but I was somehow also grateful for it. Some days, it was simply pain. Nothing to be done. That day, it was obvious that grief's purpose was to heal.

While writing, that day, because I was so isolated I had nobody to talk to, let alone about K, I realized that spending my birthdays with memories of him was how I wanted to deal with them, in future. So that's what this is, once again. Yet again, just threads and sketches; I don't know if it'll ever feel possible to write something *complete* in his memory, something which does what it needs to do. Maybe that's fine. Last year, to try to write anything at all didn't feel right, and I was too much of a mess for other reasons. From somewhere, this year, I have energy enough to write.

A few days after K died, I realised a document was missing. While he was alive I had no idea how important it would become to me, but once he was gone it was immediately obvious that I had to find it. K was a mathematician, and a private maths tutor. That was how he made a living. I've always been fascinated by mathematics, but never seriously pursued it beyond school, and he would occasionally say to me:

—Do you want a maths lesson?

Invariably, I would. He tended to accept a bottle of wine as payment, and he would share it with me throughout. We would cover simple things, simple things in new ways, things which I knew from school but was rusty with, things which I had no memory of whatsoever and which he couldn't believe I didn't know about; and sometimes, we would touch on more difficult things. These 'lessons' would become great sprawling conversations lasting hours into the night. I loved them. He was very patient with me, and I will have been very annoying sometimes. I loved all the time we spent together. I loved him.

Once, I asked him a question in the pub which he couldn't immediately answer. I don't remember what this question was, but it was related, he said, to something fun he had wanted to show me soon in any case. I'm fairly sure it was going to be an introduction to Riemann's Zeta function. My question, whatever it was, caught his imagination, and he went through several attempts to answer it. For a few weeks I would sometimes get a text out of the blue: 'It's a fractal', or 'I think it's a solid black triangle'.

I remember the evening where, having made a breakthrough, he tried to explain to me what he thought was going on. We were sat at a tiny table tucked away at the side of the pub. I was transfixed. I did follow him, but it was, to me, difficult maths; and as soon as the explanation was over, I could not recall any of it. It felt like a vanished dream. Several sheets of paper were filled, during this explanation, with diagrams, and with lines and lines of his chaotic handwriting.

It was one of these sheets of paper, the only one which somehow found its way into my house, which after his death I noticed was missing. In the days after he died, I was out of my mind with grief and pain, and finding this page became a fixation.

M

K was not there for the very start of Singing Club, in 2015, but he soon became a fixture of it, and it a fixture of his life. Mbira Club, too. In Singing Club, he was often difficult and stroppy; he would sit on the sofa and grumble, refusing to do warm-ups, and he would refuse to sing anything other than the melody. He would sing the melody in a very low octave, insisting, just as he insisted that he couldn't sing harmony lines, that he couldn't sing high. He could do both of these things, but was unconfident, and resistant to trying. We did persuade him to sing harmony, just once: not a line, but a single note, in our very own arrangement of 'The Prickle Holly Bush': one single note which strengthened the final chord of the line 'Oh it pricks my heart full sore', halfway through the chorus, and made it sound magnificent. He hugely enjoyed this one moment of harmony singing, and so he embraced it, on the stubborn condition that he would do no others.

We didn't sing that song very much, after he killed himself. It was so devastating—and so absurd: almost comical, in an extraordinary way—to hit that grand chord and hear, really truly hear, his absence from it.

K left notes in the diary on his phone, including a description of the funeral he imagined. 'Tim will do a poem', he wrote. Somehow, I did as I was told. He also wrote: 'H will sing a song'. This was not easy either, as she was far too devastated to learn anything new, or to sing anything alone; but we all spoke about it together, and H said that singing the opening solo in a song she felt safe with already would be something she could do. A fine compromise, it was felt. We all sang the Mingulay Boat Song, which K had loved, and H did the first verse on her own. It was heartbreaking, but it was beautiful.

Later that year, in the middle of summer, an all-day event was put on in his memory. His favourite local bands and soloists played, his poet friends did readings; there was a set from Mbira Club, and at some point, a set from Singing Club. We sang 'The Greenland Whale Fisheries', the 'Mingulay Boat Song', possibly some others, and the Sydney Carter tune 'Sing, John Ball'. It sounds like a folk song that's been around for centuries, but it was written in the fifties or the sixties by Carter, a committedly socialist schoolteacher who was also behind all those melodies which we of a certain age remember from school assemblies: 'One More Step Along The World I Go', 'When I Needed A Neighbour', and the infamous 'Dance, Dance, Wherever You May Be', which Carter adapted from the Quaker hymn 'Simple Gifts'.

'Sing, John Ball' is the best of the lot, for me. I was having a horrible week when I first heard that song, and the intense joy of it was exactly what I needed. It was some time in the autumn of 2017. I immediately taught it to Singing Club. Somehow, very few of us had heard it before. Everyone loved it. (As far as I know, none of us were Christians, and we all had a very easy time treating the religiosity of anything we sang as irrelevant, so long as we enjoyed singing it.) Our friend V, who only came to Singing Club once, came by chance the night we learnt 'Sing, John Ball'. Not one of us had had a good week; we were all absolutely harried and exhausted, a couple of us even tearful to begin with. By the time that evening was over, we were all walking on air, as we bounded across the road to the pub. V is a poet. At least one of her books uses for its material the words to 'Sing, John Ball'.

We had, we realised, tried it that first night in every single key, to see which one sat with our collective voices best. I can't remember what we decided, but I do know that the following summer, to end our set for K's all-dayer, we belted it out in his memory in the key of F. We slightly fucked it up, on the day, but it still made for a joyous finale.

M

One night in 2016, or 2017, tidying up after a Singing Club which K had been unable to attend, I had a look inside my violin case, which I had knocked over. It was, like the violin inside, a knackered thing. It had belonged to my grandfather. It had seen very little use from me, since I never did learn to play it, despite trying to as a teenager. From the secret section at one end, a little compartment of pitch-black felt, opened by a rigid flap of the same, I withdrew some crumbling rosin and some soft cloths. Underneath was the small, misshapen piece of earthenware with the turquoise-brown glaze, the '-1P' price tag still on it. I hadn't seen it for a decade. If I'd ever thought about it, I would have assumed it had got lost, on one of the many occasions I'd had to move house.

Online the next day I told the story of that object. The bitterly cold winter's day, the huge tall potter with the giant beard, and his purple-brown patchwork coat. His remark:

—Some things make their own way into the world. Others need a little help.

I mentioned the penny he had given me to take it off his hands. I attached a photograph of it. Under this little anecdote, K commented. He said it had made him really happy. He listed the elements: the object itself, the man who might have been a wizard, the thing he said to me, the fact that I'd just found it again. He said, once again, how happy it had made him.

An hour or two ago I looked online on streetview, for the location of the potter's stall. I found it easily. The area in front of the bookshop is empty, as it usually was. This is a mad, meaningless coincidence, but in the corner of the screen, it said that this photograph of the spot where the potter's stand had been was taken in February 2018. Of all the months it could possibly have been taken, 'February 2018' is the only timestamp which means I can stare at that image and not know whether K was alive or dead when it was taken.

M

It was in truth not long before I found the missing sheet of paper. I cried. It is a strange, gorgeous thing, a tangled mess of diagrams and equations. I haven't a clue what any of it means. I remember a happy moment, in such a sad time: I said to K's sister that I didn't have the first idea how to understand this document, that I couldn't even remember what question I'd asked, and that, in a way, I didn't ever want to understand any of it. She laughed, and said:

—Yes, that sounds very *him*.

The reason I did not find this mathematical scrawl for so long was because I repeatedly mistook it for something else. He had done his drawings and algebra on the back of the lyrics I had printed to 'Sing, John Ball'. In the summer and autumn before he died, K had been incredibly depressed. That was why he turned to the prescription medications whose side effects drove him in less than a winter to kill himself. I won't call it consolatory, but it was a very moving moment, the discovery that K, who had increasingly found it very difficult to be anywhere, or to do anything, had made it to that one Singing Club in which Sydney Carter's extraordinary song had arrived out of nowhere. To 'rescue' us, as V put it.

The most prominent diagram from K's page is in this book, at the start of Chapter 64. What a mess! I thought for a while about using it as the cover image. This book, like K's mystery diagram, is divided into four sections. For that reason, it felt appropriate—as well as the fact that K and I are owed a book together, in some sense. He read an early version of one of the longer pieces in this book, and I woke up to a string of awesomely generous messages telling me it was his favourite thing I'd ever done. He was so enthusiastic about it, he said, that he wanted to write something similar. He had his idea already. He wanted us to publish a book together: *Collaborations and Forgeries*, we quickly decided, would be its title. That book did not even come close to existing. I never saw K's draft of his story.

K's diagram, with its four quadrants and its strange diagonal streaks, looks to me like the intersection of a pair of Euclidean axes. I'm almost certain that's exactly what it is. The inscrutable diagonal scribblings on it represent attempts to answer the question I asked him, whatever that was. Somewhere on it, I like to imagine a single point.

Perhaps P (and it is P, not p) just means Pi. It isn't a pair of coordinates; it looks like a single number. Perhaps P is a bit like i, the square root of a negative, and -1P lives in some complex habitat. Perhaps it just stands for 'Perhaps'. It's impossible to know exactly where, without a scale, but the price of that misshapen ceramic thing, -1P, plotted on those axes, must lie somewhere to the left of the origin. Somewhere on the line $x = -1$. And I wonder what kind of coin the potter gave me, almost twenty years ago, if P means something other than penny.

It is the sort of thing K and I would talk about for hours. Nonsense mathematics, absolutely silly but absolutely serious, the whole worlds and shapes and narratives that would fall out of tiny glitches and surprise intersections. Simply play. Patterns and textures to reality which mattered to us and us alone, which we conjured together, and which were gone forever as soon as we finished talking about them.

So many things are simply gone. I am incredibly grateful for the artefacts I have. Somewhere on that incomprehensible diagram, itself on a sheet of paper which proves K made it to Singing Club on a very special night, I like to imagine the coordinates of the singularly unusual price borne by that object. That strange, misshapen little thing which twice, in a time of deep depression, he explicitly said made him feel happy.

77 Not a drop of it

Today, New Year's Eve, I went to the churchyard for about half an hour. I go there when I feel cracked, wrong, not sane, because more than anywhere else around here it seems not to mind. Next to each other at a shallow angle round the side of the church are two knackered benches, the flat part of each being made of two long slats of wood. One of those benches is missing the front slat, and one is missing the back slat, rendering each a ridiculous perch. I think their backs are similarly broken, in a matching or complementary way.

Often you find that this churchyard is a brief haven for people whose lives, you can tell, without even talking to them, are fucked—whether it is drugs, drink, homelessness, madness, abuse, any or all of the above. It is never busy. People are sometimes unconscious there, on the mud and the leaves, in the day. I am housed, and in that I am very lucky; but I am still a mentally ill addict, and I go to this place and feel calm, and feel like I am not going to be judged. All of which is entirely contrary to my experience of churches, of The Church, in the past.

I don't mean the church, though, I mean the churchyard. Much of its ground is raised, a metre or two above the surrounding streets, so that when you walk around three sides of it, you are on a level with the remains on the other side of the red-brick walls. Maybe you could pull a brick out and shake a bony hand in the soil. Against one of the walls parents line up waiting to collect their kids from the primary school opposite, leaning on the dead as they wait.

It is absolutely not one of those churchyards in which committee members and volunteers over the years have managed to organise the dead neatly; it is not a tidy, bright, well-tended lawn, graves lined up in grid patterns, by which the building itself is somehow prettily moated. The headstones and tombs lay at angles, chaotically. One of the stones, standing in an area where there are few others, is so worn that it's completely unreadable, and is formed from a circle above a rectangle, so that it looks like a torso and head poking out on a diagonal from the grass. Some of the trees look like they began as the shapes of people, frozen in time just as they were flayed excruciatingly into skeletons. Thick tufts of thin sucker-branches sprouting from the ground at the bases of others might testify to severe root damage; they have been let grow til they are yards long, and then been curled up into loose wicker circles, as if Sycorax is making herself known.

The church itself is a foreboding, dark, blockish thing, the blackest I've seen: it looks like it has been dipped in soot, and reminds you more of Victorian industry than of worship. I've never been inside. It does have services, it's a functioning church. The churchyard I've heard rumours is deconsecrated, and although I have no understanding of the specifics of what that means, it makes a sort of emotional sense; its solemnity seems more gnarled than holy, as if sourced from something far older than a nineteenth-century church building.

In summer, the churchyard is a wild-flower meadow, but in winter it's an absolute dark lake of ghosts. I have seen few places, even at this time of year, which look more comprehensively dead. More than just deathly, since all graveyards must be that, it looks dead, like it actually died, all at once. As if there was a single moment in which something happened to it: Death itself circled the outer walls three times, in a curse, and then walked away; a sudden obsidian rain broke from the sky above, not a drop of it outside the walls, and killed in an instant everything it touched.

Today it was wet, completely soaking wet, and the rain did feel to me as if it brought with it an appropriate, attendant darkness: even though the dusk is always inevitable on its own terms, something other was going on. I stayed there until I felt a little better. I watched a worm go across some concrete, for a while.

78 Fire escapes, pub signs

Oh fuck me I miss vodka so much. Nothing I've ever found, before it or since, is like it. There's been lots of drugs I tried to replace it with but none of them even at their most intense were the first bit of vodka out of the bottle. I'm all day always trying to decide whether I resent it or not, that if I want to have a life at all it has to be conditional on the absence of that exact moment, the first bit of vodka out of the bottle, the best thing ever. I say 'the best thing ever' about a lot of things because it's fun to be enthusiastic, and emphatic, and to do that doesn't mean it's disingenuous, but at the back of it I always know that my true best thing ever is the thing I cannot ever have, not if I want to hit 50 and then 60 and whatever else. The rest of the bottle is fun, subsidence, insights, mistakes, empathy, another bottle, beautiful chaos, bad chaos, beautiful chaos again, extremely bad chaos, then consequences, always consequences, gut-ache, not being clear-headed until sunset the next day, embarrassment, sweats, the taste of how cheap it was in the smell of what I sweat out in the shower. The start of the bottle, the very first taste, and the relinquishing of control, it is heaven on earth and always will be. I feel like recovery, if I ever achieve it, will depend on my NOT lying to myself about that. It's the most true thing I can think of about myself, and it sounds so banal, but it isn't, it's like I said, it's a brief access of heaven on earth. And it's not allowed.

2013

Summer. A very bright, very hot day. The bus from Falmer campus (Sussex University) to Brighton is busy. It's about 1pm. I should have finished in the spring but I've had to repeat a term, thanks to my drinking. On the top deck I sit in an aisle seat halfway down the bus and stare, hunched forward, at some ballpoint-pen graffiti on the yellow-cream plastic of the back of the seat in front. I am forcing the sides of my fists into each other between my thighs, and my upper arms are shaking with the effort. I am not doing this deliberately, but because I cannot help it.

My nervous system is in serious trouble. I've had about half a bottle of vodka. I used to carry it around in a Lucozade bottle, naively believing people wouldn't be able to tell. Half a bottle hasn't been enough to stop the shaking. I am staring at the graffiti as if my life depends on it, because in these situations it feels like it does. I have the image, because this is how it feels, of my nervous system being pulled as tight as possible, tighter and tighter, like the drawstring of a kit-bag, and I am terrified, without knowing what this might mean, that it will snap. That something will give. I feel like a disgusting, sweaty mass of gristle and ganglions, dehydrating under a midday sun until the elastic of some unseen tendon gives, and the whole mess explodes.

Alcohol withdrawal is a medical emergency, but I don't know that yet. I am unaware of just what danger I am in. I feel like this every single day, at some point, because I am not yet in the habit of carrying entire bottles of vodka around. The graffiti on the seat in front of me is something to focus on, as if I can somehow hook my consciousness onto it, prevent my nerves from being so tightly gathered that something snaps. I am sweating and shaking. The bus is going very slowly, and getting slower at every stop, as more and more people get on and get off. As soon as it gets far enough into town, along the Lewes Road, I can get off, run to an off licence, and buy vodka.

—You're not okay, are you?

Next to me, sat by the window, is a tiny woman. She is probably old, but does not seem it, somehow. She is wearing a gorgeous coat of an autumnal colour: deep brown, or bottle green, I cannot now remember. On her lap is a commensurately tiny rucksack, fun and brightly coloured in blues and reds and yellows, with edging and panels which are shiny and rainbow. I cannot stop staring at the graffiti on the seat in front, which feels rude, but I manage to shake my head. After a while I manage to say:

—Not really.

—I do try not to judge.

I have no idea how it happens, but I become aware that I can release my right hand from the fist it is making, slide it up, and lay it flat, just back from my knee. The woman places her left hand on it. I notice her hand and see that she is definitely old. It is very gentle. She applies no pressure, just rests her hand on mine. She doesn't try to stop her hand shaking, along with mine.

—Is it alcohol?

At this I somehow manage to breathe a little more gently, and nod my head slowly. I still cannot stop staring at the graffiti.

—Yes.

—You do smell a little of vodka.

Her vowels, very subtly, do something as they meet with her consonants, a barely-audible meniscus, which makes me wonder if she grew up in the Netherlands.

—Myself, I have terrible trouble with these.

She takes from her coat pocket a metal case, and clicks it open. It is filled with the most immaculately rolled cigarettes I have ever seen, all of them perfectly formed, identical, and kept in place behind an elastic fabric strap. Her hands may have been old, but they were obviously not arthritic.

—I smoke one every hour of the night.

I nodded. She slides the case back inside her pocket.

—Of course, I have to get dressed. Then I sit down and I smoke. It's lovely.

I can't speak, but I nod, with a big, sincere grin. It *is* lovely to smoke, isn't it.

—I get undressed, and I do need to have a shower before I get back into bed. So that's another ten or fifteen minutes. There isn't always time. Often I don't get much sleep because sometimes a cigarette takes a long time.

There was a pause, and then she said, again:

—I do try not to judge. You don't judge, either, do you.

It was a statement, not a question. I try to smile at this, with a feeble shake of the head, to agree with this negative, that yes, no, I don't. Not quite in her direction, but enough that she can see me, and I can tell she has seen me. I want to cry, but I can't, or don't.

From the front compartment of her rucksack she takes a small wallet, the size for cards and nothing else, and gives it to me. I open it up. Inside, one half has a transparent plastic window, through which is showing a printed card. It tells me that she—'This person'—has suffered a traumatic brain injury, and says that my tolerance and patience is appreciated. (Perhaps that was the wording. It's been ten years). Here are her contact details. She lives in Whitehawk. Here are some other phone numbers in case there is any cause for concern. I've never seen such a thing before, and I feel like my nervous system is about to snap, and all I can do is nod in such a way as to signal: okay, I understand. I realise I can place my other hand over hers. The entire interaction is so gentle it is unreal, as if fallen from a dream.

Soon, I stand up to let her out, because it is her stop. We smile at each other once more. She gets off the bus with her small colourful rucksack on both shoulders. I sit back down, slide over to the window, where she had been sitting, and slump, still shaking, with my face against the glass. I find myself thinking about moments which you know immediately you will never forget.

2023

One decade later, more or less. I am stepping, very slowly, unbearably slowly, down the fire escape of an incredibly tall building. Some massive gorgeous skyscraper somewhere. The ground is still weeks away. With every new step down there is time to stop, time to survey the landscape.

In this image, the height of the building is a given intake of alcohol. The ground represents what I want my intake to be: none at all. The reason I am going so punishingly slowly down the fire escape outside is because, even though I feel like I have in some sense escaped the building, and whatever chaos was inside, it is not medically safe to go from a high intake of alcohol to none at all, suddenly. Alcohol withdrawal is not merely unpleasant, it's incredibly dangerous. You can have seizures; you can die.

Sometimes I am surprised that my life didn't abruptly end, at some point, seven or eight years ago. Surprised and grateful. There were definitely times then, horrible times, when I went from multiple bottles of vodka per day to none at all, because I had no money. I'm not drinking much these days, by my standards, but even now, according to any doctor I speak to, I can't yet just stop. It's not safe.

Things may look very different, on the rickety steps outside the thirtieth storey, from how they looked up there outside the hundredth, but it's still too soon to just leap off, hoping to hit the ground and be alright.

One reason I've made any progress at all is because of where I'm living now. When my life back in Brighton imploded, I asked a friend, here, who I thought might have a spare room, if he could help. He said that he did—spare rooms, plural!—and that I could stay there. This involved leaving my old life behind and moving 200 miles away, but it was my only option in the circumstances. He rescued me, is how I see it. I put all my stuff in storage until I could find somewhere to live. I lived for two months out of a suitcase, and tried to find somewhere to live in this new city.

Having lost three or four minor income streams in the pandemic, I survived at this point on disability benefits alone, which meant I wasn't accepted for a viewing. Not one. Most of the flats I looked at explicitly demanded a minimum income of some insane figure. Those that didn't, when I rang up, either disclosed only at this point that I needed to be earning a certain amount, or told me that the flat was already let. This minimum income threshold, as I am sure you know, is a relatively new strategy which landlords and estate agents have developed which replicates the classist and ableist stipulation 'no DSS', now that they are no longer legally allowed to say that. If the rent itself isn't already high enough for *Local Housing Allowance rates don't cover the rent on this property* (in Brighton, this was, even then, every single one-bed flat on the market) then they just say, to make absolutely sure, 'you must be earning this much to be eligible'—and then set it prohibitively high.

I got summarily turned down more than twenty times in a row, and grew more and more despairing. My friend suggested that my living in his spare rooms became a longer-term arrangement. For that I am going to be grateful forever, because I was very ill, and I was out of options. I do not like to think where I'd be, or what state I'd be in, if he had not done what he did.

There is a fire escape—a real one, in this case—which can be accessed from the window right by my bed. It begins with a metal platform, with railings, and then there is a ladder. I haven't ever tried to climb it, not in either direction. If I did climb down it, I'd not reach the ground, because it stops in a roof garden on the first storey. Specifically, it stops in a beer garden. Yes: this life-saving spare room is above a pub. I've never had alcohol in the pub, because in this new reality I don't do crowded indoor spaces without masks; and besides, I think that would be a very, very stupid seal for me to break, psychologically. Maybe this summer I'll manage a lime and soda, outside, in the beer garden.

M

Why am I taking it so slowly? Why don't I just get help, go to rehab? Stop, completely?

That is exactly what I tried to do. There are medical interventions can take place, in order that you can just stop drinking, immediately but safely. A private inpatient rehab, possibly, if you have the money; or, for those of us like me, who don't have hundreds let alone thousands of pounds to spare, an outpatient one.

I've done an outpatient detox before. You attend a fortnight of weekday-morning meetings and are given, on each day, chlordiazepoxide, generic trade name Librium, in a dosage gradually titrated downward by experts, according to your need. This drug makes you feel pleasantly woozy—in the past, I remember, it made my appetites for both food and sex go through the roof; I spent the afternoons and evenings of those outpatient detoxes having a wild time on Grindr. The point is that the process enables you to suddenly but safely stop drinking. By day fourteen, if things have gone well, you are teetotal. Perhaps earlier, if you weren't drinking so much. Fourteen days, done.

At that point, let's hope you've already put some sort of aftercare in place. Whatever the addiction hub in Brighton was called, over the years—CRS, then Pavilions, then Change-Grow-Learn—it was absolute chaos, administratively. But you'd get on a detox, and hopefully then stay sober. In 2019 I did just such an outpatient programme, and was teetotal for five months. That was my longest ever. It was remarkably easy, staying sober. I was incredibly happy to be sober. I wrote a lot. I got a few more jobs, and negotiated them with the Department for Work and Pensions without being punished for them. I spent as much time as my health would allow me walking in the countryside, and read books with a clearer head than ever. That summer, I did acid once and MDMA twice. They were never the problem anyway. I did ketamine five or six times before realising that it threatened to become its own problem. But I was sober, so I was able to simply stop taking it. Being sober was a success, for as long as it lasted.

I don't know what has changed, or whether it's simply that I'm in a different part of the country, but my experience this time round is that detox programmes now are ferociously gatekept. Instead of simply having long waiting lists—they've moved on from saying, 'We'll help, but it'll take a while'—they simply say 'no'.

This was revealed to me in spring 2021, when having had to leave Brighton, and having existed in the rooms up here above the pub for five months, I decided that I was only going to make a new life here if I stopped drinking. For good. People trying to be helpful will say to you: Can't you just ask your GP for the drugs? You can't, and I am sure for good reason. Those drugs, misused, are just as dangerous. You will always—and this seems to be true everywhere—*always* be funnelled to the local addiction hub. All roads lead there. I'm making that point now, deliberately: this place is your only option. Your only port of call.

It should have been fine. I did what I was advised to do: went through my GP, got a referral to the local addiction hub. I didn't equivocate; I didn't say I wanted to see if I could become an occasional drinker. I said that I wanted to stop drinking. I said that my entire life had fallen apart, that I was in a new city, where I knew almost nobody; and besides that, the entire planet was in lockdown. I said, the only way I'm going to pick myself up and build a new life here is if I stop drinking. Right now. They lost me in the system once or twice, and cancelled several appointments without telling me—all too familiar, but a perversely cosy feeling; it made me nostalgic for times spent with K and S at the Brighton addiction hub, incredulous together at yet another appointment lost in the system—but after a month, I was assigned a key worker. They rang me up, and almost straight away they said to me:

—I'm not going to recommend you for a detox. I think you might start drinking again.

That's how it began. I'm fairly sure I said, Okay, but I don't want to drink. I want to be sober.

—I think you might start drinking again, though.

I realised, unexpectedly, that having finally got an appointment with someone, I was actually going to have to make a case for wanting to stop drinking. I've got to this point in my life, I said, and it's taken a lot. I really, really, really want to be sober. It's the only chance I have. I will attend whatever groups you want me to. I just want to stop drinking.

—I hear what you're saying, but if we detox you now, you might start drinking again. So I won't be recommending you for that.

So, I asked, what do I do?

—I think you should cut down.

This repetitive conversation lasted, no exaggeration, months. I asked for an outpatient detox, so that

I could stop drinking, and my key worker said they wouldn't be recommending me for that. Repeat. So many times in the last two decades of my life I have tried to cut down. It hasn't worked. It's pretty much the reason I call myself an alcoholic, the fact that by no effort of will have I been able to drink any less than 'to oblivion' every night.

Before this encounter with the addiction hub, I'd never before been told that the decision to stop drinking, which is not an easy decision, was the wrong decision. I've spent most of my adult life having people say to me, You *have* to fucking stop drinking! And now that at long last I agreed with them, the only place that could help me stop drinking was refusing to. It was the same response, over and over.

—I'm not going to recommend you for a detox, because you might start drinking again. I think you should cut down, instead.

Over these months I found myself pleading with my key worker personally. Why would I be asking to stop, if I was able to cut down? Do you think I haven't tried to do that *a thousand times* in the last decade and a half? Would I have got to this point in my life, of begging an addiction service for help to stop, if I was in any way able to cut down? I want to stop drinking.

—I do hear your frustration, and I understand that you want to stop. But if we detox you, you might start drinking again.

Trying to reason with my key worker, I confessed that sometimes, within months of having done a detox in the past, I had started drinking again. Except for that one occasion. In 2019, *when I lived alone*, I was teetotal for five months. I started drinking as soon as I began flat-sharing again. This is why I was so dead set on living alone. Right now, I said, I am living alone. I know what I need, in order to do this. It's taken me a decade to learn this, but I know what I need for it to work, and that's why I now live alone. *I've left my entire life 200 miles away so that I can live alone*, for this reason. I want to stop drinking.

They got angry with me. They began to condescend to me, began to treat me like an entitled little brat, simply for asking for help and knowing what kind of help I wanted. Please, don't think I don't appreciate how overworked the people at an addiction hub must be, and how nasty and unpleasant their job must be sometimes. Their role in this situation was evidently to refuse me the detox I was asking for, unless I somehow proved myself worthy of it—by doing something I already knew I couldn't do, and which would in any case have rendered the detox unnecessary—but they went so far beyond that refusal, talking to me as if I was a spoiled child, as to be by far the rudest professional in this context that I've ever encountered.

It became upsettingly clear to me that helping wasn't the point. They simply wanted me to 'engage'. Engagement seemed to mean being kept in prolonged stasis, stuck exactly where you are, so long as you kept a precise record of the manner in which you were stuck. It felt unpleasantly like a shit job, and certainly didn't help. Presumably then, after some undisclosed time period, and according (in the manner of PIP) to an undisclosed mark scheme—or, I don't know what's worse, on someone's whim—you *might* be allowed onto a detox programme.

With this key worker in particular I got the feeling that the demand wasn't just that I engage, but that I be obedient. *You'll learn about yourself,* they kept saying. They were insisting that what they were offering was help, and what I was telling them was that it wasn't, and I strongly felt that they resented me for saying so.

What happened next, though I didn't realise it for two years, finally undid what little mental health I had left. In a subdued but docile mood I rang up and told my key worker the truth, which was that being refused a detox, told to cut down, with the support of one phone call a week, wasn't helping me very much. So, understanding that the addiction hub could offer nothing more, I had arranged to check in, online, with a few friends, every single day. I was pleased with how it was going, and was very grateful to have friends who'd agreed to it. In response:

—Well, what's the point of that? That's not coming from you, is it?

The following day I rang up and asked for another key worker, but it was too late. As I say, I didn't realise it at the time, but this, as minor as it sounds, was the moment that triggered a total breakdown. Everything caved in on me at once: two decades of drugs and alcohol, the unprocessed harm from several abusive partners, the suicide of my closest friend. Being 200 miles away from home in a city I didn't know, during a global pandemic. My life already in tatters, the addiction hub had refused to help me for months on end, and now they'd angrily told me that the support of my friends was wrong, too. So I fell to pieces. I lost my mind.

M

For six months already I'd been isolated and alone, like so many of us had at that time. I barely went outside for another two and a half years. I got groceries delivered, if I remembered to, and could afford it. I mostly couldn't, obviously, so for a while I ate one meal every two or three days. I drank more, and less well. Worse than I ever had. I became malnourished, but I put on seven stone. For eighteen months my days were one long panic attack. An old inner ear problem reared its head and gave me relentless vertigo, possibly because of lack of vitamins, and possibly because for years on end I never saw anything that was more than six feet away, let alone a horizon.

In August 2021 I removed my mask in a queue for half a second and a few days later tested positive for COVID-19. Although the illness itself was mercifully mild, probably as I had just been vaccinated, the two years of after-affects were not mild. That first attempt to rejoin the land of the living went so badly that I still haven't. Not really. More than three years, barely speaking to anyone. Only five or six times since leaving Brighton have I had physical contact with another person. I have absolutely no idea when I will have a sex life again. There are people, shielding since March 2020 and still shielding now, for whom this will be the case for the rest of their lives, because of what has disgustingly been called 'freedom'.

There is a misconception that those of us who survive on benefits have a lot of free time, because we don't spend forty or more hours a week at work. We may even spend no hours a week at work. From 2020, that's been my reality. What is left, some people need to understand, is substantively different from what is called 'free time'. For my part, if it were 'free time', I would have done things. I'd have watched films, read books, written music, gone for walks. I'd have kept in better touch with people. I'd have noticed and named my breakdown quicker; I'd have recovered quicker.

Almost all of what people imagine to be free time is actually, for many of us who survive on disability benefits, time occupied by suffering. Everyone's suffering is different, but it must be universally true that time spent suffering is exhausting, such that what little time is left over is compromised and ruined in its wake. I do not want to die, I thought, but this may be more than I can survive. Panic attacks so bad that I spent most days thinking I was going to die anyway. Every day, for two years, I thought to myself: if this is forever, I'm going to kill myself. I thought this knowing very well the effect that becoming a suicide can have on those you leave behind.

M

The last time I did anything social, in the before-times, was on February the 8th, 2020. At the time I was, for a month, escaping a hellish relationship and accommodation situation by living on K's boat. It had lain empty since he had killed himself, but had been lovingly maintained, and the mooring paid for, by two friends. Living on that boat was one of the worst times in my life. It was also one of the strangest and most magical.

That night I'd cycled into town. Many of us were in the pub, The Heart and Hand, in the middle of Brighton; it was a joint birthday gathering. It was busy, and wonderful. Everything I miss about normal life. At one point, approaching 11 p.m. on February 8, 2020, I stood outside The Heart and Hand, smoking a cigarette, and noticed that in the incredibly strong winds the pub sign was swinging. Swinging and squeaking.

When later that night I got back to the tiny but infinitely safe space of the Rebel (so the boat was called), I got undressed, and snuggled up under the duvet. Moored in the marina, the Rebel and I were rocked about and jostled in the water: something clanked sonorously above, and the shadows inside shifted and lozenged about, dizzyingly. The winds were that high. I took out my phone, played the recording I'd made of the squeaking pub sign—only just audible, above the sound of conversations spilling from indoors, and the growl and hiss of strong winds over a tiny phone mic—and I wrote down the tune it was playing. I've lost that piece of paper, but I remember the detail closely. I am glad that I wrote it down, not for that reason, but because it fixed the fact of the squeaking sign in my memory.

Recently, I was sat by my window, above this pub, 200 miles away from Brighton, and heard a loud squeaking which I couldn't identify. After a fruitless search around the rooms up here, I looked out of the window, at the right time, and realised it was this pub's sign, squeaking in strong winds.

Once again I am pretending there's a pattern. During the breakdown I tried desperately to find patterns, every single day. When I found one I would cling to it. If something calmed a panic attack, even only slightly, I would grab a bit of paper and try to write down what I'd done, in ludicrous detail, and stick it on the wall. The flat became absolutely covered in notes-to-self which were nothing more than mad and mostly failed attempts to cope. That's all it was, just trying and failing to cope. Maybe that's what this entire book is doing.

This is one of its longest chapters, and certainly its most arduous. Having tried to console myself at length with imaginary fire escapes, pub signs unexpectedly provided something more personally meaningful.

Maybe, if one squeaking pub sign signalled the start of the worst years of my life, the ending of my feeling like I existed—what if another pub sign squeaking, mere feet away from me, is the signal that I can return to life? At last. What if? I'm *deciding* that it does mean that—that I've waited long enough, that it's a little smile from the universe, delivered via un-oiled metal and strong winds.

Why else would I have bothered, three years ago, to record the sound of a pub sign, and to write down the notes it played? I pretend that I was reaching back from this dismal timeline, saying to myself: pay attention to this. It might help later. This is, by the way, one of the less insane ideas I've had about how to understand my last two or three years, how to cope with them.

I'm still drinking, of course. For almost one year now I have been checking in online, daily, with a group of friends who have known me at my very worst, and are forgiving, wonderful people. I still live above the pub and will still never drink in it. I will forever owe an immense debt of gratitude to the friend who gave me somewhere to live, and to the friends who I check in with every day. Often I'm a kind and gentle man, easy to tolerate. Sometimes I am a bitter, furious, snarling monster. I wish I wasn't, and I try not to be.

Of course I also try not to be angry with the hub, and with the one key worker in particular who knew better, who refused me access to help. I asked them for help to stop drinking, and instead they triggered a breakdown which lost me years of my life. For such a long time I was barely even a person—but still suffering, of course, and still getting older.

Like I said, I try not to be angry. But I fail. I hate the addiction place for refusing me help. Someone I know, a recovering alcoholic and an AA sponsor, told me that he's been in contact recently with a young lad. Bright, brilliant, beautiful, not yet twenty, this boy: and he has near enough drunk himself to death. As it has done with me, alcohol has seen him hospitalized multiple times. Unlike me, he's also been sectioned, possibly more than once. You'd think that something as awful as being sectioned would earn you a place on whatever programmes are available. His addiction hub have refused him a detox. They're forcing him to cut down, to prove himself worthy of their help. My acquaintance, the AA sponsor, said:

—He's going to die. They're refusing him the help he needs, and he's going to die. There is no doubt in my mind, he is going to die.

Nobody's ever given me an explanation as to why these places are the way they are. Is it money? Ideology? Top-down spite? All of these things? Why are these people in these jobs? They must know they're making help conditional on the one thing you can't do—otherwise you wouldn't be begging for their help. I just wish they wouldn't slam the door in your face with such relish.

I cried at that young man's story. All evening I kept remembering it and kept crying, each time. Never for a moment had I assumed that my situation was unique, but to have just one anecdote of someone else having the door slammed in their face, by the only people you can go to for help: that was enough for a dam-burst of tears. The heady combination of heartbreak and hopeless rage is so familiar, in this miserable country, and so asphyxiating, just as the Tories want it to be. I wanted to hug him, I wanted to make everything better for him, because even the people whose job it is to do that were coming up with reasons to consign him to oblivion.

M

Ten years ago an old woman on a bus placed her hand on mine, and told me she didn't judge, despite the fact I was shaking, and was dripping with sweat. She placed immediate trust in me, enough to tell me some details of her own addiction. She was a wonderful person.

I mention her again now because I found myself wishing I could be, to that young man, the brief presence she had been to me, simply because she made me feel hope. That you can be that old, and that broken, and still cross two unfathomable mental distances—sat on that bus together, we were both so far away from the world—in order to be unforgettably kind to someone.

The idea that one squeaking pub sign signalled my life being put on hold, and that another squeaking pub sign signals the start of a new life, a period of reassembly after a period of total collapse—I don't care if that's a flimsy, stupid, contrived little emblem. It is an emblem for my having hope, and hope is a tough thing to have, living as a skint person in this Tory shit-hole, let alone as an addict. There's many thousands of people who are less lucky, who never find a way through. It shouldn't be lucky, the fact I'm supported by friends and am therefore not going to die, despite the fact an addiction service, the only port of call, refused me help. They caused a breakdown, rather than helping me avoid one. That shouldn't be how any of this works. It just shouldn't.

Nevertheless, I am very, very lucky. I am not out of the woods yet, but I have some sense that there is a way out. That this isn't forever.

One day maybe I'll be able to live by the sea. The cost of renting means it's probably never going to happen, but that's the one thing I want. All hopes and ambitions for careers, creativity, for doing anything whatsoever with my life, have collapsed into the black hole of the breakdown, so that my one remaining dream is to one day live by the sea. By the sea—or maybe, once again, on it. I should write about that boat.

79 A party

On my long walk home there was a party in the street. It was winter, it was cold, the sky was a pure and icy black. The air was so clear it felt ready to chime, and its clarity was brittle and immediate, as if something might crack. The night, you felt it on your skin, was everywhere, on everything, preparing with its moonlit vapoury confederates all the upward-facing surfaces—the houses and the tarmac and the parked cars—for the more overt frost of the dawn. You could witness what had been your breath, as it met with this brittle clarity, and briefly joined it in a vanishing flurry of the only other colour, which was silver. It could have been any time of night, but it seemed somehow that midnight had been recent, like Christmas. Despite this the new day, like the new year, felt a way off.

For some reason, the party was not inside, nor in the front gardens, and I couldn't tell which house it was in. You do assume that a party is based in a house. This one seemed not to be. Perhaps eleven houses had decided together to have a party. There seemed to be that many houses in a row with the lights on, glowing out onto the same side of the street. In front of them all was the party, and the long party was wide too, wider than the pavement, it spilled a yard or so into the road. Outside one of the houses must have been some powerful speakers, because all this was to the sound of 'Starships' by Nicki Minaj. It was one of the long, steep, residential streets running almost the whole distance between Fiveways and the bottom corner of Preston Park. It feels posh: the houses look spacious and grand, with big bay windows.

Not one of the other houses had any lights on. The party—I don't want to call it a street party—but it was a party, in the street—felt rare and precious, like an inhabited planet—a freak of life in the deep stillness and dark—and it could absolutely not have been impromptu. The party in the street was planned, for sure. It simply must have been planned, because everyone had dressed so beautifully for it. Not ostentatiously, but beautifully, and all in black and silver, as if to match the sky and the stars and the moon, and the vanishing breath and the lingering cigarette smoke. I envied them their cigarettes, but I would smoke when I got home. It was a little like a perfume advert, except that everyone was drunk and high. Three or four of the boys were in long black dresses, to match the girls. For sure, some at the party were neither; and every single person was too beautiful to feel the cold. I noticed collar bones, arms, shoulders, and the finely shaped backs of exquisite necks, some of them decked in the most delicate jewellery.

I don't know why I walked through it, rather than around it. There was no traffic to stop me walking in the road. It was a beautiful gathering, for the beautiful, and I suppose I wished for a moment to be among it, even though I never could be, never could have been, part of it. Not a class anxiety: they were not, or were not required to be, rich people. They were beautiful. They seemed to be students who were enjoying dressing up—but they were all so gorgeous, together and individually, that it didn't even occur to me to try to talk to anyone, to try to join in. Some of the beautiful party's beautiful bodies were moving with the music, though nobody was dancing to it, not quite. They were standing in groups of three or four, and I had to weave between them, stepping off the pavement into the road, and back onto the pavement, and back into the road. A beautiful boy of about twenty said,

—Excuse me!

And pressed his fingertips onto my shoulder.

—Excuse me—do you have any filters?

I didn't speak, but I nodded and smiled, pulled a box from my pocket, and gave him and his cute friend, who had leant in and clearly wanted to ask the same of me, two sticks each. They were briefly grateful, but the interaction was over. They were so gorgeous, so fluent in and completed by their bodies, that it didn't even occur to me to desire them. Which probably is the least hurtful way it could have happened. I know now that at the time I was attractive, but I couldn't see it. None of this was for the likes of me.

Someone stumbled slightly and their wine spilled. I ducked out of the way, silently, stepping down into the road; but his friends leapt back noisily, celebrating the surprise adventure of an escape of liquid as if it had been the sudden flurry of a stressed bird. This time, I hadn't made any eye contact.

Now the music was 'Pursuit of Happiness' by Kid Cudi. I hadn't realised, not until that moment, how much I liked it. Now, the song and the party remind me of each other. The chorus contains its own echo of that ancient warning that not everything which catches the light is going to be gold; and here it seemed simply true, a straightforwardly literal fact, as if a lyric could be accidentally photographic: the party, like the night, was edged and flecked with dazzling detail, but none of it was gold. All of it was the same brilliant silver. After about a minute, I had walked through the party, and was out of the other end of it.

As I walked on, down that steep street, not yet even halfway down the hill, boots creaking, I stood still. Suddenly I had remembered running out of filters that morning. All day I had been roaching, ever since. I checked: there was nothing in my pocket. I turned abruptly round, and the party was gone. The street was silent and still. No lights were on, no music was playing, and nobody was dressed in black and silver, looking stunning and joyful.

M

This awesomely vivid hallucination was the closest I have ever experienced to something I might call seeing ghosts—the closest I have to a ghost story of my own, although it isn't one.

It was as simple as doing a lot of drugs, and being far too often awake for days and days on end. Not hallucinogens, but the frequent sleeplessness was so extreme that it made me hallucinate people—though usually only individuals. Sometimes, retroactively: several times when I recalled a night or nights of chemsex (this was the addiction, the reason for the drugs) there was, in the memory, the impossible presence of an incredibly old woman. She was always seated and turned away, wearing a heavy shawl of black and purple. Once or twice I wondered whether she was me, at the very end of my life, visiting.

It was difficult, at first, to believe that the party had never existed. Difficult and profoundly sad, like waking from a dream in which you had been in love to a life in which you are lonely and alone.

But it was certain. The street was perfectly silent, and absolutely still, in pitch-black and brilliant silver-white—the moon at least had remained real. I could see my breath, and now in the silence I could even hear it. I remember staring back up the street for barely five seconds before realising I wanted to cry.

Refusing myself the tears I turned and walked on, down the steep street. The rest of the way home, another twenty minutes, I looked only at where my feet were about to land. I remember being surprised even then at just how sad, just how absolutely lonely I felt, trudging home after the beautiful vanished party.

They had all been such glamorous ghosts. What if I'd tried to join in, and had felt alienated and mocked, as usual? What if I'd tried to join in, and had been welcomed? Only for the party which had allowed me into it to vanish after a too-brief minute. I don't know which would have been worse. Being disdained and excluded by those gorgeous ghosts—or, to have been let in, to have enjoyed a rare and precious feeling of belonging—then suddenly a silent empty street, and the hectoring reflections of a hostile moon.

Whatever questions I can ask of it now, a magical reality had been closed off, my access to it permanently slammed shut. When I got home, I drank vodka and smoked cigarettes until I passed out with my boots on, the same as every night.

80 Letters

Here we are, in a small room, with a book. We'd like to tell you what we know about it, and what we don't.

In a second-hand bookshop somewhere off the Caledonian Road, in the summer of 2015, one of us found an edition of Théodore Garrigou's *Letters*. It is a paperback of 192 pages, translated and edited by Jules Thibault and published in 1994. It is not an elegant book. The cover is pale yellow, with the word 'LETTERS' in bright red capitals, in a chunky sans-serif typeface; in the same typeface at the bottom of the cover is Théodore Garrigou's name, in white. The printing has not quite matched up, giving the lettering a blurred edge. It was printed and bound by M.F.P. Design Print Ltd., a now-defunct enterprise based at the time in a trading estate just outside Manchester. Our best guess as to the publisher or imprint are the two words 'Melikerion Talea', which appear only once.

We found Théodore Garrigou's *Letters* shelved among books about mysterious and unexplained phenomena—for the most part, books about crop circles—in a section marked 'PARANORMAL'. It seemed to belong to a collection of about thirty books, which had presumably arrived in the shop at the same time, but had not yet been properly sorted: Garrigou's *Letters*, which appeared to be the exception in this strange assortment, never mention crop circles, and indeed do not deal in any immediate sense with the supernatural. Like its shelf-mates, this book bore on its inside cover a small white sticker, giving in rather austere gold lettering a name, and the address of a house in Lewes, Sussex. We suspected that the redistribution of these books was the result of a death, and later confirmed this to be true.

There is no note on Théodore Garrigou, nor on the translator, Jules Thibault. The book proceeds, after the title plates and publication data, without even a contents page, straight to the Preface. Thibault's Preface is only a few pages long, and begins with what appears to be a disclaimer:

> It is only after considerable anxiety and soul-searching that I have decided to publish the letters Théodore Garrigou sent to me. Those who go looking in Mr Garrigou's letters for anything more than they already know will be disappointed.

Thibault sketches—briefly, but with much sincere admiration—the early life of his colleague-turned-friend. We learn that Théodore was born in Poitiers, on January 7, 1954, and that he was a brilliant student from an early age—a polymath, indeed, in what Thibault only just stops short of claiming is a manifestation of true Frenchness. Garrigou's school days were unruly, but he hit his stride as an undergraduate, despite taking several attempts to complete his studies and changing his field of study repeatedly.

To begin with, we suspected this entire volume was a self-published project in which Jules Thibault would settle a dispute with Garrigou regarding something called 'Garrigou masks'. Thibault's Preface worries at them, but the letters themselves mention Garrigou masks infrequently. Only once are they referred to by that name, except to confirm what Thibault asserts, only with far more good humour than he does: Garrigou masks do not exist. A Garrigou mask, says one letter, is

> simply the fiction of a death mask fashioned in some unaccountable hurry—that is to say, while its subject is still alive—the death of which subject is hastened in order that they may be a decent likeness of their mask.

Various versions of this fiction, Thibault says, give different, spurious reasons for the mask being made too early; perhaps the clay is due to dry out, or even to run out. It doesn't matter, as Thibault says three times: the point is that this broken little fable constitutes an analogy, or metaphor. For quite what, even after repeated readings, we aren't sure.

Thibault does not reproduce any other account by Garrigou himself of what a Garrigou mask is; nor does he clarify how, or when, or where, they were so 'violently and tendentiously misunderstood'.

In 1982 we find a statement from Garrigou which is grandiose, if a little cryptic, in which Thibault preserves the French spelling of 'mask', for some reason:

> Jules. My enthusiasm for the masque is a dead fox. I am bored, J! A. says I am stressful and makes unreadable faces. I would not be the first person who has told a parable braiding scarcity of resources with the privileging of IMAGES over LIVES and has then been got wrong.

'A.' is the sculptor Agnes Germain, who with her husband Didier had taken young Théodore in as a lodger while he was still an undergraduate. Their mentions in his *Letters* are frequent, and generally much more adoring than this. It was obvious that they remained on good terms.

After this letter, so-called Garrigou masks are never mentioned again. If this was what Thibault meant, in warning 'those who go looking' in these *Letters* to prepare for a disappointment, then he was right to do so. Yet it is Thibault's own Preface which offers them as such a tantalizing mystery. He asserts the following, which initially seemed dubious or extravagant:

> Neither will any French speaker have heard of [a Garrigou mask].

but which took on a different character, the further we read. The reference to a language is significant. The preface ends, perhaps a little sadly:

> I do not pretend that I believe this to be a useful document, and you will read more than once that he thought me mad to keep a word of it—but Mr

Garrigou's friendship has been of much comfort to me, and I have always looked over this archive gratefully. I have partially reproduced it for the general reader, in the hope that even if he is looking in vain for what is not there, he may nevertheless find something in it.

M

Théodore Garrigou's *Letters* evidence a rich and lively correspondence—one side of it, anyway—beginning in 1979 and continuing for almost fifteen years. The book may, broadly, be divided into three sections.

The first four years are the letters of a confident, accomplished young scholar. Garrigou has finished his studies—at the Université de Poitiers—and has moved, in the first of many uprootings, often sudden, to Paris. He writes to Thibault, his former tutor, several times a month, and, over the years, their collegiate relationship, always undisguisedly warm, becomes trusting and close. Garrigou has several jobs, mostly but not always academic jobs, over this four-year period, and moves around a lot, but still writes regularly.

For the next five years, in the mid 1980s, Garrigou appears to have settled down. His letters over this period are confidential and intimate. The two men's scholarly rapport has segued easefully and touchingly into a sustained dialogue—a friendship—of profound confidences, of unhesitant disclosure, and of kindly, tender questioning.

The documents in the third and last section, however, from around 1987 until December 1993, are less frequent, and fast become markedly different. Garrigou is not so exuberant, and his bounteously camp references to friends and to events—his gossiping—becomes less prominent. His brash and cantankerous verve seems to diminish, and along with it so does his impetuous wit, and his joyous, scampering enthusiasm for the world. By 1991 his letters no longer seem even to be part of a conversation. They occur more sparsely, but the prose itself becomes much denser.

Aug 25. 1991—

To Jules T.

For SIX the horsehead nebula; for FIVE the weather here in blades and torrents, you do remember the path along the cliff, where we nearly came to grief?—for FOUR the pleasure of yawning off the rig; THREE and in perpetuity my difficult nervous heart will prevent me from sleeping. Memory melting likewise into fingers, the inward textured wax irrupting, sliding on the surface of dark absences and vivid mixing so to sink into itself. The stars are snowing. TWO—As with all things, distant and deep and met always unawake: ONE, what a noise a nebula makes!! Yours ever. TG.

Reading further into the 1990s, to call these documents 'letters' at all feels incorrect. Théodore Garrigou seems to have been posting a poetical scrapbook. It is difficult to tell the extent to which he is any longer writing in response to his friend, or even whether he continued to receive Thibault's letters. We realised we did not even know whether Thibault kept writing them.

Having no other instincts, we heeded Jules Thibault's advice, and did not look any further into the story of the masks, deciding instead that Garrigou himself was the greater enigma. Reading to the end of the volume does not clarify anything. That the communications of the early 1990s, the last stretch of the volume, are increasingly fragmentary and esoteric, does seem coterminous with a lessening of frequency and intensity, a tailing-off, but equally there is no sense of a disagreement or an estrangement.

There seemed to be no explanation of why this correspondence disintegrated. Surely it would be negligent to publish the correspondence of an esteemed colleague, let alone a dear friend, without mentioning the occasion, if not the circumstance, of his death. Perhaps Garrigou had been institutionalized. His later letters are chaotic, even disturbed, as if his reality is fraying. We seem to be in very different company. Whatever happened, Thibault tells us nothing.

At the back of all this, simply as readers encountering a volume for the first time, we had a strong feeling that something was being kept from us. What was Garrigou's discipline? What was the subject of his doctoral thesis? Most importantly: why don't we get to read Jules Thibault's own letters? Where are his replies, the documents which would complete, or at least illuminate, these dialogues with Garrigou?

To this last, we did find an answer. In a very brief communication from Jersey in 1981, which must have been a postcard, since it begins

> Much my view, but a little less sunny, and facing the other way!!

Garrigou exclaims:

> I know you are a hoarder, of almost all your post. Why? At any rate. Perhaps instead of a cabinet or drawer, this one may find its way to brightening your miserable desk a little.

The incredulity Garrigou expresses about keeping letters seems, here as elsewhere, to refer chiefly to his own, but we can reasonably assume that those letters he received found their way to the bin. Otherwise, our early research revealed no answers—especially as to why he seemed simply to vanish in the mid 1990s.

It was not merely that we couldn't find any reference to Théodore Garrigou's death: we could not find a reference to Théodore Garrigou. Neither any mention of a Garrigou mask—anywhere. Not one of the universities we contacted (three French, one English) had any record of him. Not as a guest lecturer, not as an employee. Why sustain such a bold and confident lie to his friend?

M

In November 2016 we were in Berlin, working on another project. Our accommodation was the temporarily empty flat of a friend of a friend. On our second evening, on one of the shelves in the bedroom, we spotted a copy of a book by Théodore Garrigou. It was in Polish. It was a translation of his *Letters*. Less prominently placed than in the English edition, buried in what must have been a preface or an introduction, was a name we recognized: Jules Thibault.

An attempt was made to request that we borrow the book, but our friend's friend never responded, neither while we were in Berlin nor once we had returned to London. For a while, we forgot about it. However, the following February, a copy of the Polish edition of Théodore Garrigou's letters arrived in the post. It had cost us more than $230 from a bookseller in Midland, Ontario, and while still readable, it had been badly water-damaged in transit. It was, as far as we could tell, the same as the copy we had found in Berlin.

It was at this point that Garrigou's *Letters* began to splinter. We noticed that things didn't match up. The Polish volume was implausibly short—only 146 pages to the English volume's 192. The dates on the letters in one book were not to be found on letters in the other. We asked another friend, a Polish speaker, if they could tell us what was missing—why the books were different. After mere minutes of flicking through them, our friend bluntly said:

—They aren't the same book.

Letters were not missing, nor were they just organised according to another scheme. The books were *completely* different. It was spring 2018, and we had only just discovered that Théodore Garrigou's letters to Jules Thibault, as collected by him and translated into English, bear no relation to those in the Polish translation. Our encounter with this book had barely started.

We now had two tasks ahead. We must firstly track down any other translations of this book which exist; and secondly we must consult Garrigou's original letters. We must at least compare the two editions we did have with the original French.

As of spring 2024, we have not found the French edition. Indeed, as we will come to in a minute, we have reason to suppose that there is no original—that the French text of Théodore Garrigou's Letters never existed. However, by 2022, we had found three further volumes of his *Letters*—'translated' into Hungarian, Finnish, and Russian. The longest is the Russian, at 212 pages. A brief glance at the dates will indicate that these books are not versions of each other. With a little help, we began to form an image of Garrigou's *Letters* existing in five languages—and any French edition which might exist seemed less and less likely to be an 'original' from which these other volumes were translated.

Perhaps 'translation' was the *canard* here. Could Théodore Garrigou not have simply been an ebullient correspondent in multiple languages? There seemed no reason why he couldn't. But why, if that were the case, make the claim that they had been translated?

The four non-English books held a further surprise. If we take a snapshot at any point during this fifteen-year correspondence, and compare between languages, then Garrigou's tone and character are consistent, even though they change over fifteen years. However, what we can read of Jules Thibault, the friend to whom these letters are addressed—his character, and his circumstances—differs wildly.

In Garrigou's English-language *Letters*, Thibault seems to be a friendly, dedicated, affable, but fundamentally lonely man, who found it extremely difficult to form friendships outside of academia, and never had a family. He is a talented pianist, with ambitions of studying organ improvisation in the French tradition, but a frustrated composer. In Garrigou's Finnish *Letters*, Thibault seems to have been married, and to have had two children, who he loved deeply, but with whom he struggled to communicate. Music is never mentioned, but he is a keen painter. As a Polish reader would encounter Jules Thibault, he is an excellent singer and violinist, and (uniquely among the five books) a very heavy drinker. He had intense and chaotic relationships with many women in a short space of time in the mid 1980s, but sustained an uneasy and covert relationship with two never-named male lovers for almost a decade.

Not everything is different, though: there are points of correspondence, between and across these distinct correspondences. In 1990, in three languages, we have letters mentioning the city of Poitiers. It seems to be the case that in February of that year, Jules Thibault moved back to his hometown. Like Garrigou, Thibault grew up in Poitiers. However, Garrigou implies in English that Thibault returned there alone and lived in a garret. In Finnish, we read that he bought a three-bedroom house.

M

Théodore Garrigou seemed to have left no trace. All we had were his letters to Jules Thibault, as collected by Thibault and published, for some reason, in five different languages. These 'translations' are completely incompatible with each other.

We began to realise that some of Garrigou's anecdotes were not his own. Here is an anecdote which he recounts twice. In English, he writes it on December 11, 1988:

> Let me tell you what I am reminded of this evening. When I was a child, my grandmother taught me how to make candles. My mother was wary, and the endeavour was kept entirely a secret from my father, who would not have approved. We made them in many shapes and colours, more than we could ever burn without giving ourselves away.

> So in fact we used simply to melt them and use the wax over again. Eventually the wax would become tan-brown, then muddy coloured. By far my favourite candles were made by pouring the wax into a cylinder which contained already an amount of crushed ice. My grandmother would give this magical assemblage a single brisk stir, and we would quickly fix the wick (just a length of string tied round a pencil) and leave it to set. What always seemed an age later, my grandmother would remove the cylinder, and the melted ice flowed away into the sink (once, onto her dress) and the candle now hardened seemed full of lesions—streaked with beautiful caverns where shards of ice had been. I always loved them. As objects—they relied for their completion on the vivid trace of something vanished.

In a similar story in the Finnish book, two months later, Garrigou describes candles made using crushed ice; but in that letter, however, he says he was taught not by his grandmother but by his great aunt, on a family holiday to Switzerland when he was almost seventeen.

As with everything about Théodore Garrigou's life, we have nothing else to go on. It was as if he had never been alive—and that was what we were coming to believe. What we do know is that Jules Thibault was very fond of an elderly aunt, in Switzerland, and that he visited her many times as a young teenager. We also have reason to believe that as an adult, he continued occasionally to make candles, but our only source for that is the Russian *Letters*.

The several versions of Garrigou's *Letters*, which by now we believed to be distinct works of fiction written by Jules Thibault, seemed to flicker in and out of reality, as if their narrator is travelling down a darkened street, and only every now and again passing under the illumination of a streetlamp. More prosaically, Théodore Garrigou's story—his stories—are full of holes.

M

We'll close with a few remarks on the increasingly fragmentary letters of Garrigou's last six years, and their strange poetry.

> Keep your mind in hell, and despair not.

So ends a letter supposedly sent from Garrigou to Thibault, in English, on the 20th of September, 1992. This, in fact, is an unattributed quotation. The author is Silouan of Athos, who is never mentioned in any copy of *Letters*, and nor is he (so far as we can tell) quoted again. This moment is curious for another reason: at no point prior to this does the exact same sentence occur in Garrigou's *Letters*, on the exact same date, in all five books. On that date in 1992—in English, in Finnish, in Hungarian, in Polish, and in Russian—we have letters to Jules Thibault which end with some variation of 'keep your mind in hell [and] despair not'.

Another such phrase, occurring on the same date in different languages, and becoming a familiar refrain in Garrigou's later *Letters*, is the simple question

What on earth can they be?

It appears first in Autumn 1990, only in the English book. Its first instance between multiple languages is on January 19, 1991, and it occurs many times throughout the last three years, as well in Garrigou's last English letter.

Not only do we know that this is a quotation, we also know where it comes from. We know this because Jules Thibault footnotes it. That he does so seems to be a gesture of relinquishing: a confession, almost, of his sustained fiction. It is not just that 'Théodore Garrigou' is fixating on a single phrase—that phrase is lifted from the writings of a man who shares his surname.

Félix Garrigou was born in 1853 in Tarascon-sur-Ariège. He was a physician, hydrologist, and pre-historian. He visited the caves at Niaux in 1864. The cave paintings there have long been recognized as masterpieces of Quaternary art. Even though he had recently visited the rock shelter of Bruniquel, in the Tarn, and therefore definitely knew about Paleolithic art, all Félix Garrigou wrote in his diary about his visit to Niaux was:

> There are some paintings on the wall: what on earth can they be?

Why this grabbed Jules Thibault so much is a mystery, but over a century later, in the letters he attributed to 'Théodore Garrigou', the repeated construction is the same—identical even at the level of syntax. The voice remarks, or asserts that there exist, some strange phenomena—sometimes more phantasmal things, such as the answers to unsolved problems, sometimes simply ponderings or hopes. These are then immediately followed by a colon, always, and the quotation from Théodore Garrigou's namesake:

> what on earth can they be?

On the 26th of February, 1992, Garrigou writes, in English:

> There seemed in that moment to be ideas—they comfort, they vanish like ghosts. Who one is when one is writing: what on earth can they be?

The phrase, in whatever language it appears, is always an awkwardly literal version of the six English words 'what on earth can they be', rather than an idiomatic equivalent phrase. The following week (in Russian) Garrigou writes:

> I feel them very strongly, my consoling selves: what on earth can they be?

Thibault's footnote, in the English volume of Théodore

Garrigou's *Letters*, led us to the 1959 English-language version of Annette Laming's book *Lascaux: Paintings and Engravings*, translated by Eleanore Frances Armstrong, which although it quotes them does not give any further details for Félix Garrigou's diaries. We can't know how or where Jules Thibault read Félix Garrigou's diaries. We think it's likely enough he first read them in this English translation, rather than in the original French.

This led us to ask another question: why did Théodore Garrigou never correspond in French? Or rather, the modified question: why did Jules Thibault never conduct a correspondence with a fictionalized image of himself, as Théodore Garrigou, in French? We have no answer—except to say that just once, he did. A short text appears near the end of all five versions of Garrigou's *Letters*. Those letters to which it is attached vary drastically in content and in tone from language to language, but they are always dated May 19, 1993. This English version is our own:

> Candles and water should be present too
> nothing is as big as a horse except another
> and there are none left
> in the field running down from the track
> or on the further hill
> at the rip of grass the snow has stopped

Not only is this the only piece of writing we have in Garrigou's native language—if he can be said to have one—these five lines constitute the only poetry he left us, in any language, which is not explicitly attributed to someone else. The character of Théodore Garrigou certainly seems to have enjoyed poetry; and his tastes, curiously, were not especially similar to the tastes of any version of Thibault we encounter in the books. Yet nowhere else is there the merest suggestion that Garrigou, or Thibault, wrote poetry.

In whichever language one reads Garrigou's *Letters*, this poem always appears in French. Jules Thibault never translated it, as far as we are aware; if he had done, it would perhaps have been the only genuine 'translation' of an original French 'Théodore Garrigou' which Thibault ever produced.

The same week we rendered that poem into English, there was a curious revelation, which cast the five books of *Letters* in a new light. We noticed that the date on which it was written—surely a coincidence—was also a significant date in our biographical sketch of Agnes Germain, the sculptor with whom the character of Garrigou had supposedly lodged in the early 1980s.

Agnes Germain—*née* Marchand—did not meet Didier Germain until 1990, in Poitiers, and she did not use 'Germain' until they married, on May 19, 1993. In all five 'translations' of Garrigou's *Letters* there are multiple references to Agnes by her married name, and mentions of her husband, as if they were already cohabiting, many years too early.

Jules Thibault must have written every version of Théodore Garrigou's Letters after that wedding. These five volumes collapsed vertiginously into a feverish writing project of no more than seven months.

M

Where Théodore Garrigou came from we may never know. To read him has been like stepping in quicksand. First, he seemed to have been a vibrant figure in many lives, for a decade and a half, especially to Jules Thibault, his friend. As we looked closer, he seemed to have become a sustained fiction. At last, we accepted that Garrigou existed only briefly, to a man who had imagined his company, and hallucinated his friendship, in an unhappy burst of intense energy. This is the final letter in the English book, dated December 31, 1993:

> Pulled apart at the fringes to a pool of sleep this time a single inward full of verticals, perhaps trees. Perhaps the legs of unfinished ocean rigs. Empty distances sliding over and through each other so as to disconnect like water in pulpy threads now reattach without qualities. The white hawk, the shrieking mast. Great convulsions of unimaginable fragility: what on earth can they be? I look up across the cosmos through the wall. They say when we do that we think we are thinking or think we are remembering. Everything so calm for the longest while then this. Suddenly a walk.

In January 1994, Jules Thibault committed suicide. He was fifty-two years old. It was a Friday, and it would have been Théodore Garrigou's fortieth birthday.

Each version of the imaginary correspondence with which Thibault left us is so different from the others that they must be taken as five distinct books—giving five distinct accounts of two men's lives—of which every word may as well have been fiction, and of which every word was written in the last year of Thibault's life.

Here we are still, in a small room, with a book, and also with four of its cousins. We don't know why they were published the way they were. We don't even know how Jules Thibault got them published. We do not know whether they are one thing, or five things. What on earth can they be?

81 Back to the sea

On this of all days my true love gave to me a crisis in the wireframe of the very sea surface and made me watch as it crashed shattering itself about a headland, one that meant something particular and special to both of us but which from that moment wasn't going to have any information about any of itself ever again stored by any surface of the sea, on any day of Christmas; we as if together had as if for years toughened ourselves and each other pocking into that sea our lives: how over what fractal fur of the headland we on and off had flaxlike crawled, and to look now to that sea among the set of all eternalizing surfaces to click and whirr away our index, what now had ever been less concave and what ever less imprintable, we asked, which is how it happened that the wick of our boundedness was of a wading: what a catastrophe it was and how mundane once we had done it, the beautiful savage inhospitable sea a boring funk of pure-pitched overwriting lap which chilled us to the clicking flooded moon, etched a scoring round our hardening blueing torsos as we stood stilled sunken and stored forever nothing of us in its surface; and how inaccessible how frozen yet how together still our feet beyond our sight way down there were.

82 Boat ride

The very lowest part of the inward boat, far below and yet still touching my back as we sway on the surface here in the near total dark and my inward eyelids wracked far below yet touching still as if another skin that newly each time invisible black before or of the sky as the water shifted under, far below my inward eyelids yours too lay closed over on our calmed and pitiful behalf some memory of what in sleep, this even as sleep seemed permanently inaccessible to proof, is yet and reassuringly the very lowest part of the inward of the very lowest part of a boat far below in the near-total dark and the kissing sea velcro of our eyelids there.

83 Farewell

Here at a wooden gantry moonlit but not moonlit enough we arrive and must stop, this slatted structure which doesn't admit for disembarkation, doesn't admit for anything, nothing, no possibility for anything at all, only the reassuring inertia of an unseen and irrelevant derelict, the occasional lovely absconding frog or flying fish, or the click and lap of equally unseen equally irrelevant halyards heard in the distance and in any case inaccessible: what we need is a holiday, or seventy-three holidays, is to mark this moment with a buoy, or thirty-seven buoys, or thirty-seven moments with thirty-seven buoys, or just a good night's sleep, a sudden walk, a last look, a headland, a boat ride, some sort of wooden dock, a lovely frog, a flying fish, both of them gone, moonlight, a derelict, every thing an abscondment, and disembarkation as a permanent condition reassuring inert unseen without click or lap underwater and away.

Notes and acknowledgements

The first epigraph is the last paragraph of section 44 of *The Pillow Book of Sei Shōnagon*, 'Things That Cannot Be Compared' (translated by Ivan Morris). The second is by Herman Melville, from Chapter 9 of *Moby-Dick*, 'The Sermon'.

Occasionally in this book there are playful little references to mathematics. If they read as if I don't know what I'm talking about, it's because I don't. You'll forgive me for not running those sections past a mathematician. The only person I want to ask is K.

Before anyone, I must thank Jon Blyth, who let me live in the rooms above his pub when my life fell apart in 2020. Nothing I've done in the years since would have been possible without his kindness.

This book is not ordered chronologically, but if it were, it would divide about halfway through. Everything written before the 2020 autumn lockdown was written when I lived in Brighton, where I was incredibly lucky to cut my teeth as a writer in an exciting, welcoming, and encouraging set of intersecting scenes, both in Brighton and from further afield. Trying to thank everyone individually for that world would be silly, but they know who they are and I send my love. I will thank Ruth Harrison and Daniel William Jonathan Mackenzie specifically, for permission to quote them.

Everything in this book from 2020 onwards was written in total isolation. I would have had a far harder and far lonelier time without the virtual company, the friendship, of Salomé Honório, Mark Francis Johnson, Bob Kingsley, Peter Manson, Mike Wallace-Hadrill, and Conrad Westmaas.

My love and thanks to them, and also to Sam Cutting, Ellen Dillon, Ian Heames, Joshua Jones, and Kev Nickells: brilliant writers and musicians, as well as wonderful friends, who gave me not only encouragement but awesomely clear-sighted and helpful feedback as I tamed this chaos-demon of a book.

In the past—years before Pilot Press existed—Richard Porter and I were collaborators. We made the most extraordinary and precious of theatre work. I will never forget it. I feel we are owed many more such collaborations, and am overjoyed that this book marks the end of a time which circumstances forced us to spend out of touch. He too provided invaluable comments on the manuscript at various stages, and I believe this book would never have been published if he had not taken it on. Chapter 66 is addressed to him, and even though it is somehow almost seven years old, its final paragraph is as true now as it was then.

Finally: as this book goes to print, I have been sober for one hundred and nine days. It's just over a year since I wrote Chapter 78. For the extraordinary and still novel feeling that I have a future at all, I will be forever grateful to Emily Best, Sam Cutting, Chris Davies, and James Dibley. This gang kept me going when I was so deep into my addiction that I had no hope whatsoever that I would escape it, especially when I hit repeated brick walls trying to get professional help. They were there for me, every day, helping me do the single most difficult thing I have ever done. I checked in with them, online, for five hundred and nine days, before I got sober. There followed an autumn and winter of chaos, but my last drink was on December 31, 2023.

It's almost summer now, and I still check in every morning. I send the date, then '0 units', with a blank line and an emoji. It's a fox. Fox means recovery! I'm not sure why. Every evening, I still check in with how much alcohol I have in the flat: 'None'. It has been many years since I saw any of these friends, and I hope it is not that long again before I get to give them whatever kind of hug it is you give to someone who has saved your life. They absolutely did that. My drinking ruled my life, and there is not one syllable in *Candles and Water* free from its duress. Whether I want it to or not, publishing this book constitutes a valediction to alcohol, a very long time coming. For that reason, it is dedicated to the four friends who helped me get my life back, with all my gratitude and all my love.